Energetic Tai Chi Chu

C000258560

By Larry Johnson, O.M.D., C.A.

Cover Illustration - Rosario
Desktop Publishing - Patricia Elste
Photography - Kathy King

Published by White Elephant Monastery
Copyright (C) 1989 by Larry Johnson All Rights Reserved
P.O. Box 523
San Francisco, California 94101, USA

First Printing 1989
Printed in the United States of America
Library of Congress Catalog Card Number 89-050605
ISBN Number 0-924071-01-X

Note to Reader and Disclaimer

About the Author

Larry Johnson has been involved in energetic work for more than twenty years. His work began with training in Chinese Martial Arts and subsequently expanded to include Oriental Medicine, Chi Gung and Meditation.

In 1976, he began a yet continuing study of Wu Style Tai Chi Chuan, Taoist Chi Gung and Meditation under the private tutelage of a Taoist Master from the Hua San School.

In 1978, Larry was given the title Sifu, or Teacher, by Ming Jew, the most advanced disciple of Lau Bun and present Grand Master of the Hung Sing Choy Lee Fut System of Kung Fu.

After completing a seven month acupuncture study program at Chakpori-Ling in 1977, Larry continued his study of Oriental Medicine with Peter Lam until 1978. Larry graduated from the North American College of Acupuncture in August, 1980 and from the California Acupuncture College in 1982. Also in 1982, Larry passed the California State Examination for Licensed Acupuncturist. He has practiced Acupuncture professionally in California since that time.

On the 15th of December, 1983, Larry received his Doctor of Oriental Medicine (O. M. D.) degree from the California Acupuncture College.

During succeeding years, Larry has continued to attend seminars and to study with the goal of expanding his knowledge of Oriental Medicine and finding new applications of this knowledge to benefit a larger segment of the population, especially those involved in one of the energetic development paths.

Acknowledgements

I would like to thank my Taoist Sifu and Ming Jew (Grand Master of the Hung Sing Choy Li Fut System) for all the help and encouragement they have given me over the years.

Each in his own way has provided me with the necessary tools to continue my path.

I would also like to thank all those with whom I have trained and shared the experience of learning.

A special thanks to Cecilia Rosario for modeling for the photos and putting up with me as a training partner for over ten years.

Parents, teachers, friends, martial ancestors - all richly deserve more gratitude than words can convey. May our hearts be one in peace.

Relax

The Chi is unlimited

Table of Contents

Introduction

Why another book on Tai Chi Chuan?

As practitioners, we have read many books on Tai Chi Chuan and although many of them are both interesting and valuable they seem to cover the same material. There is a section on history and philosophy, a section on the form and its usage, and a section on the classics and their interpretation.

The section on history and philosophy is usually interesting but holds little new practical information. The section on the form is undoubtedly not the form we are practicing or looks quite different from the way we were taught so it to may be interesting but has little practical value. Finally, the section on the classics and their interpretation is like all the other such sections we have read, interpreted the same or slightly differently and explained in a way that does not lend itself to any new practical understanding.

The purpose of this book is to present a different view than the regular fare of Tai Chi Chuan books and hopefully, offer some new practical insights and techniques that we all can use to help develop ourselves through our art.

My own Sifu studied Wu Style Tai Chi Chuan under both Wu Kam Chun and one of his accomplished students. He also studied Taoist Chi Kung, which is his specialty, under a Sage from the Hua San Tradition.

The techniques and theories presented here are gleaned from my studies in Oriental Medicine, the teachings of my Sifu, and the practical experiences of twenty years of Chinese Martial Arts training.

May the presentation of this material be benificial in helping others to find their WAY.

History of Tai Chi Chuan

Tai Chi Chuan, or Supreme Ultimate Boxing is one of the finest products of Chinese philosophy. It is a system of fluid, rounded, balanced movements based upon the principles of the Tai Chi diagram, the Five Elements, and the I Ching.

The historical origin of Tai Chi Chuan is not altogether clear. Most authorities give Chang San-Feng, a Taoist and Tai Chi Chuan teacher born in 1247 AD, credit for originating this unique system of exercise which aims at harmony of mind, promotion of health, and attainment of rejuvenation and long life.

Several styles of martial arts similar to Tai Chi Chuan existed before Chang San-Feng, including Yin-Gin Ching, Hsi Sui Ching, San Hse Chi, Hsien-Tien Chuan and Hu-Tien Fa. All these styles contain elements of Tai Chi Chuan but Chang San-Feng, who is known to have studied other styles, achieved the union of these styles, Chi-Kung (Taoist breathing techniques), and the principles of the I Ching and the Five Elements to form the complete Tai Chi Chuan system.

Various schools and styles of modern Tai Chi Chuan trace their origins through many generations along diverse pathways back to Chang San-Feng.

The chronological history of Tai Chi Chuan has been well presented in many other books and needs no further elaboration.

The original eight postures are said to represent the eight trigrams of the I Ching and the five directions are correspondences of the five elements of Taoist Philosophy. Together these are generally accepted as the thirteen original forms.

Some authorities believe that Tai Chi Chuan originated as a set of static postures which were later combined to form the moving sequence. Over a long period of time new techniques were added to the moving sequence resulting in the Tai Chi Chuan long forms we see today.

Now the tendency to add to the Tai Chi Chuan seems to be reversing itself and some experts are presenting shorter versions of the set. Yin at the extreme changes to Yang and Yang at its extreme changes to Yin, the cycle continues.

My Sifu believes Tai Chi Chuan developed from "The Eight Ways of Tai Chi Breathing", a powerful and far from static exercise in his system of Taoist Chi Kung.

The truth may never really be known, but it is reasonably certain that from a small number of basic positions sprang the multitude of styles and interpretations of Tai Chi Chuan we see today.

Being aware of the history of our art is important for several reasons, not the least of which are showing respect and giving thanks to those who came before us.

One of our other main interests in the history of our art is trying to comfort ourselves with the knowledge that our historical lineage had a recognized Master reasonably close to our generation.

There are several main styles of Tai Chi Chuan today and they appear quite different in form. Since many of them do have renowned Masters in their lineage it is difficult to pronounce any one style superior to the others. It is commonly accepted that if the style follows the basic precepts and principles as stated in the Tai Chi Classics it is valid.

Students often try to use the historical lineage of a particular style to choose a Sifu. Unfortunately this is not a foolproof method. The fact that a certain teacher spent thirty or forty years (or claims he did) training with an acknowledged Master does not mean he has acquired the way of the art. On the other hand, the fact that a teacher has spent less than ten years with his Master does not mean that he lacks understanding or expertise.

What is certain is that even with a good teacher one must spend hours a day training for many years to grasp even the rudiments of Tai Chi Chuan. Without grasping the rudiments it is difficult to teach the art.

Another interesting aspect of studying the history of Tai Chi Chuan and its practitioners is the light such such study throws on what it takes to develop properly. Stories of training methods abound in the historical literature and being aware of this information helps to give us a realistic view of the time and effort necessary to develop exceptional skill in this art.

Training Tai Chi Chuan

Assuming that serious practitioners are training in Tai Chi Chuan for energetic development, it is important to take a look at what this can mean—and cost.

The result of training correctly for a long period of time is supposed to be the harmonization of body, mind, and spirit with each other and with the Tao. In other words we reach a state of oneness with nature—"In the Tao" as my Sifu would say.

This process of becoming one with the Tao is not an easy one and the practitioner will inevitably go through many stages of physical, emotional, mental, and spiritual growth before realization of the goal. Growth is often painful. Growing pains will be experienced in varying degrees throughout the training process.

Physical pain

Physical pain is very common to most practitioners as a direct result of the physical use of their bodies. The long hours of training necessary to progress on this path will generate a good deal of "sore muscle" pain.

As the body is called upon to channel greater amounts of energy, it will restructure itself to its "natural" condition. This restructuring process can be painful and discouraging. It can be difficult to distinguish between the restructuring process, injuries, and painfully incorrect training methods.

Old injuries that may not have healed completely will often reappear with the increased flow of vital energy. This can be a sign of a more complete healing taking place but will still cause discomfort.

Because we use the physical body throughout much of the training process the potential for discomfort will always be present.

Emotional Pain

Emotional pain can also be generated by training Tai Chi Chuan. Ultimately the increased, harmonious flow of Vital Energy will balance the emotions but here again the process of change and healing can be uncomfortable.

The Vital Energy that is developed and circulated throughout the body as a result of proper training will access the internal viscera. Each viscera has an emotional aspect that will eventually be brought into balance by this circulation of Vital Energy. That balancing process can be difficult. Old injuries of an emotional nature may have to be healed on a deeper level. During the healing process these old emotional traumas can reappear just like old physical injuries. Every level of our being must be brought into harmony to achieve the goal.

On page 44 of Hara Diagnosis: Reflections on the Sea by Kiiko Matsumoto and Steven Birch we find the following quote; "Looking for an underlying emotional trauma requires the assumption that the emotion really is distinct from the body and its symptoms. For the Oriental Practitioner this is really approaching the problem backwards, since the dualism itself is neither seen nor acceptable."[1] This quote illustrates the Oriental view that physical body energy and emotional energy are inseparable. That inseparability is the reason that correct energetic training is one of the surest ways to resolve deep emotional disharmonies.

Mental Pain

Mental pain comes in many varieties along the path. For instance changing our life-style to fit the needs of serious training can be very difficult on the mind. It can seem as though we were giving up a great deal to pursue our goal and often the mind rebels at the seeming sacrifice.

The mechanics of training day in and day out, year after year place heavy demands on the mind. The discipline involved is extraordinary.

Progress in training relies heavily on mental participation. Each new stage of development reached places a new and different burden on the mind. The circulation of Vital Energy helps the mind accept and enjoy training but the mind must constantly increase its awareness and control to promote increased development.

In the beginning years of training, just trying to practice the physical forms correctly affords fairly steady progress. Later in the training process much more is needed.

When the forms are fairly correct and sufficient physical strength and endurance has developed, attention to detail becomes the key to progress. Every part and function of the body, energy, and spirit must be scrutinized by the mind to bring them into harmony through the classic principles of Tai Chi Chuan. This makes training more and more difficult.

Awareness always increases faster than ability if we are training correctly. Therefore, one part of our mind continually experiences us as getting worse and worse for our efforts rather than better and better. This is both painful and frustrating to the mind.

If you find a practitioner that believes he is very good you have probably found one that is training incorrectly.

Doubt is always undermining our minds. We wonder if our methods are correct, if our teacher is knowledgeable and if he is, will he really teach us. We wonder if we are training enough and if we are emphasizing the most important aspects of training in the time we have. We wonder if we can see clearly enough to make the correct choices for our progress, realizing that incorrect choices can result in ten-twenty- or thirty years of training without real progress. And of course we look at what we may be missing by having chosen this path and wonder if that choice was wise.

Perhaps the most painful and valuable mental hurdle we must cross is the realization that our progress is our own responsibility. The teacher cannot give us energetic development, we must get it ourselves. Even training with the best teacher will not bear fruit if we do not take the personal responsibility for our own progress. The principles are written in the classics for all to understand. The teacher we have chosen (wisely we hope) is there to help guide us but the bottom line is we have to put in the thought and work ourselves.

The final "pain" for the mind occurs in advanced stages of training where it must be stilled and relinquish itself to "spirit".

This is like a parent preparing a child to face the world. The love, devotion and bonds involved in the preparation attaches the parent to the child and makes to difficult to let go.

So too with the mind. The love, devotion and hardship of nourishing the body, spirit and energy to the point where spirit can take over the direction of endeavor, attach the mind to the result of its work and makes letting go is very difficult.

Spiritual Pain

Shen is considered the guiding spirit of man. It resides in the Heart and activates and controls all of the body processes. In being involved with all the other body processes Shen can be affected by them. Thus if imbalance occurs it can disturb Shen. Shen can be depleted by energetic dissipation and strengthened by energetic development.

Through the correct practice of Tai Chi Chuan, Shen will be strengthened and along with the rest of our energetic being brought into harmony with nature. As with other levels, any old damage or imbalance to the spirit that remains unhealed will have to be repaired bringing the possibility of a painful period of change.

As various parts of our being are brought more closely into balance our life-style, awareness of ourselves, and relationship to the world in which we live will gradually change. Shen is closely associated with the emotions and can be addicted to experiencing emotional extremes. As our emotional imbalances begin to correct themselves and our life-style begins to change, the spirit can become threatened and begin to resist the changes. Because of its control aspect and access to every part of our being, Shen often begins to provide situations and relationships that can interfere with an intense training schedule. In its threatened state it seeks to limit that which is causing the changes. It may even go so far as to try to totally prohibit training, thus progress. It seems as if forty nine and nine tenths percent of Shen is trying to stop our training and we only have a tenth of a percent to keeps us at least evenly motivated on the path. In fact the majority of people who start training drop out after a number of years.

Shen is often in a somewhat comfortable circumstance- it is used to its condition and resists change. This is one of the reasons so many people quit training just when they are beginning to make some real progress. The Shen does not want to trade an entertainingly unbalanced emotional climate for an unknown and possibly less excitingly addictive state. The Shen enjoys drama!

Tai Chi Chuan is an almost magical tool for personal transformation. Because it is an ordered approach to development on so many levels of our being, Tai Chi Chuan offers a unique opportunity for us to become naturally integrated beings. Through training we can rid ourselves of the extraneous baggage of a lifetime (or more) and bring ourselves into a state of harmony with the Tao.

The situations that Shen provides for interfering with training can also be used as tools for advancement. The important point to remember is to stay on the path — keep training. If you have your goals set clearly and continue to train with purity and determination the goals will be realized.

Despite the discomfort on so many levels, the situations needed for your continued growth and development will always be provided. It is up to you to take advantage of them by maintaining an open mind, a positive attitude, and a steady desire to persevere in your work.

Energetic Philosophy/Physiology

In the Tai Chi Chuan classics and other explanatory works on the art a large number of Chinese terms relating to energetic philosophy are used. The single terms are interpreted and explained individually but I have yet to see the overall energetic systems of the body presented. It is very difficult to grasp the meanings and relationships of the parts without a view of the whole. Appreciating the intricacy and cohesion of the whole energetic system is a good way to dispel the confusing mystery of the parts and show an ordered path towards energetic development within the system.

I am not a scholar of the ancient Chinese characters. The following translated material is taken from various sources in both the medical and martial communities. Scholars themselves often disagree on the precise translations of many of the old works. My purpose is to use some of these translations to point the way to an intellectual grasp of the subject matter in English. The real method of understanding is direct experience which is beyond any language. May my intellectual inadequacies offend no one nor mislead anyone.

On page 156 of <u>Extraordinary Vessels</u> by Kiiko Matsumoto and Steven Birch[2] we find the following diagram.

Diagram A

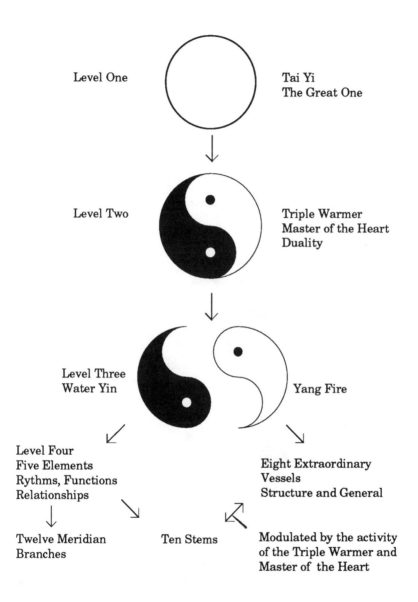

Level One — Tai Yi / The Great One

Level Two — Triple Warmer / Master of the Heart / Duality

Level Three / Water Yin — Yang Fire

Level Four / Five Elements / Rythms, Functions / Relationships — Eight Extraordinary Vessels / Structure and General

Twelve Meridian Branches — Ten Stems — Modulated by the activity of the Triple Warmer and Master of the Heart

This diagrammatic model is a useful tool for our explanation of the overall energetic systems of the human body.

In the martial community many authorities view body energetics in the following manner.

Diagram B

Level One — Wu Chi

Level Two — Tai Chi

Level Three — Leung Chi

Level Four — Five Elements — Eight Trigrams

Let us take a closer look at these four energetic levels. The proper understanding of these levels can bring the focus of our training into perspective, answer many of our philosophical/ physiological questions, and ease our minds about the mechanics of development through Tai Chi Chuan.

Level One

Wu Chi - Tai Yi

Wu Chi is said to be the state that prevailed before the Universe existed. It was from Wu Chi that the universe and all that it contains began to evolve. The Wu Chi was a Thing of nothing. It is beyond the ability of the intellect to conceive of Wu Chi.

Lao Tzu called this state TAO.

In the first verse of the Tao Te-Ching we read: "The Tao that can be told is not the eternal Tao. The name that can be named is not the eternal name. The nameless is the beginning of heaven and earth."[3]

In the following quotation from Hara Diagnosis: Reflection on the Sea, by Kiiko Matsumoto and Steven Birch we see that Tai Yi and Wu Chi have the same flavor if not the exact same scholarly translation.

"The one, Yi — is often synonymous with Tai Yi; the Huai Nan Zi says of the one:

The Dao begins at the one.
The one itself does not create.
The one divides and becomes yin and yang.
Yin and yang unite harmoniously, subsequently everything is created (HNZ3:167)".[4]

Level Two

Tai Chi

On page 71 of Hara Diagnosis: Reflections on the Sea by Kiiko Matsumoto and Steven Birch we read; "In tai ji the basic qi is still blending before heaven and earth divide. [5]"[5]

Both of the Level Two diagrams show the classic Tai Chi symbol

which graphically depicts the interplay of yin and yang. As soon as anything manifests from Level One we have the opposites — something and nothing—yin and yang.

Level two, as stated in the quote above, is the state of harmonious interaction before yin and yang differentiate. Both yin and yang are present but un-manifest as separate entities. This state is not the Tao because our intellects can grasp its existence.

There are several terms in the above quote that must be more clearly understood including qi (or Chi), basic qi, heaven and earth.

Chi

In regards to ch'i we quote Manfred Porkert, "Nevertheless the term ch'i comes as close as possible to constituting a generic designation equivalent to our word "energy"." Again from Manfred Porkert, "And yet unlike our concept of energy, ch'i, whatever the context and absolutely without exception, always implies a qualitative determination of energy. In other words ch'i means energy of definite (or definable) quality."[6]

From these two quotations we understand that ch'i is a term used for energy and that energy always has a definite quality ascribed to it. This quality is determined by the use of the word. For example we can have the ch'i of the lung, or the ch'i within a certain food, or the ch'i of a tree.

Basic Qi

Regarding basic qi, we read in <u>Hara Diagnosis: Reflections on the Sea</u>, "this idea is very similar to the concept of Tai Yi as that from which everything emerges and is created, since the basic qi is like primordial qi from which all else comes."[7]

Porkert defines "primordial ch'i" in two ways, the second of which is relevant here. "Undifferentiated potential of cosmic energy, chaotic or primordial ch'i." [8]

From these quotes we understand that basic ch'i is the underlying energetic strata of all creation from which yin and yang and all further manifested phenomena arise.

Heaven and Earth refer to yang and yin, the two opposite yet complementary basic forces of the universe. These opposites will be discussed in detail when we reach Level Three.

Because heaven, earth, and man are the three levels of existence commonly accepted by early Chinese scholars it is logical that heaven and earth were mentioned as the first representatives of yang and yin. Man is thought to be a composite development of these two manifestations. It is interesting to note that these two opposites do represent up and down and that many Tai Chi Chuan forms begin with an up and down movement. The inner alchemy of internal development also depends on the up and down movement of various energetic entities for its fruition.

One pertinent point is referred to in Hara Diagnosis: Reflections on the Sea as follows, "Summarily, the source, the root of the twelve meridians, is the place where earth's energy reacts with heaven's energy." [9]

This quote tells us that the place where heaven and earth's energies react or interact is the source. This links the source with Level Two—Tai Chi.

On page 112 of Hara Diagnosis, Reflections on the Sea we read; "There is a clear relationship between the basic, fundamental qi and the source qi. Basic qi is the "enfolded or implicate" order, the source qi is the first unfolding of the basic qi." [10]

Later in the same paragraph we read; "The basic qi is the prenatal qi while the source qi is the root of the postnatal qi." [11]

Here we see that source qi is the first development from basic qi just as in humans the source qi is the first developmental manifestation of their existence -- their root.

Oriental medicine views the source as both the energetic and physical center of the body. It is located in the Hara or abdomen at the place called the Tan Tien, the moving qi between the kidneys, or the gate of breathing. The first energetic and anatomical location of the human body is the Tan Tien. Ming Men is anther term closely associated with the source. Tan Tien is the name of an acupoint on the abdomen in front of the "moving qu between the kidneys" and Ming Men is an acupoint of the back behind the "moving qu between the kidneys".

The source is like our battery. It provides the basic energy on which all other systems in the body operate. When it is exhausted we die.

Source qi can be exhausted by illness, overwork, excess sexual activity, trauma, and the improper functioning of any of the other energetic systems of the body.

The source qi is used in the digestion of food and in turn is nourished in part by the product of that digestion. It is also used when the qi from the food we eat and the qi from the air we breath is transformed into vital energy for the body to use.

Source qi is necessary for the energetic transformation resulting from proper training in Tai Chi Chuan.

When the overall energetic systems of the body are working harmoniously, enough energy will be produced to operate the body effectively. Any excess energy will be stored in the kidneys and can be used to nourish the source.

If the energetic systems of the body are not functioning properly or extra energy is needed to fight disease, trauma, etc. stored energy from the kidneys will be used and eventually the source will be depleted.

Another method of nourishing the source is through breathing, particularly deep abdominal breathing.

Improper breathing can deplete the source just as proper breathing can nourish it.

It is interesting to note that those who practice certain forms of Chi Kung involving deep abdominal breathing often experience vibrations in the area of the Tan Tien. This vibration, which truly is a "moving qi between the kidneys", is said to occur when the source is nourished to the point of overflowing the Tan Tien and traveling through the other energetic channels of the body to nourish and heal it. This same vibration can be experienced in the practice of Tai Chi Chuan.

The Tan tien, Ming Men, Gate of Breathing, and moving qi between the kidneys are all intimately and directly connected with the source, first evolvement of the basic chi and both physical and energetic center of man.

Triple Burner and Pericardium

If we look at the medical communities diagram (see Diagram A) we see that Level Two is labeled Triple Warmer/Master of the Heart Duality. The Triple Burner and Pericardium are depicted as corresponding to Level Two. These functions are said to have a name, but no form.

"The idea of no form does not simply refer to absence of material substance. It refers to the essential change of state between matter and energy, to the basic underlying substrate of material existence." [12]

This quote from Hara Diagnosis: Reflections on the Sea informs us that the Pericardium/Triple Warmer complex is instrumental in the active energy-matter-energy transformation of the body.

With their philosophical/physiological position at Level Two on the chart, they are concerned with and essential to the most profound energetic transformations initiated by the proper practice of Tai chi Chuan, mediation, or Chi King.

A thorough explanation of these terms is necessary to grasp the importance of much of the philosophy of the energetic development of Tai Chi Chuan.

Triple Warmer

The common view of the Triple Warmer is that it has no material organ associated with it and generalizes the functions of three major anatomical areas of the body.

The upper warmer refers to the respiratory and circulatory functions of the body and is anatomically located in the chest.

The Middle Warmer refers to the digestive functions of the body and is anatomically located in the abdomen above the navel.

The Lower Warmer refers to the reproductive and excretory functions of the body and is anatomically located in the lower abdomen below the navel.

"The Triple Warmer has its origin in the Hara and is the source of Chi of each of the meridians and organs." [13]

Here we see the importance of the Triple Warmer in relation to the other meridians and organs. It links them to the source both by providing them with source chi and by its overall involvement in energy transformation in the body. Both the Triple Warmer and the Pericardium (which we will discuss next) are links which connect the source to other aspects of the body.

The Triple Warmer brings source chi to the extremities of the body as well as to the organs. This concept has been accepted by the medical community and commented on throughout the medical classics.

There are several other, less well known, functions of the Triple Warmer that make it extremely important in the practice of Tai Chi Chuan or any other energetic discipline.

On page 144 of <u>Hara Diagnosis: Reflections on the Sea</u> we read, "These ideas were clearly stated in 1813 by K. Mitsutane in Kaitai Hatsoumou. He stated that the triple warmer is related to the lymphatic system of the body, specifically the upper warmer to the thymus gland, the middle warmer to the pancreas and the lower warmer to the systems of the lacteal ducts, especially the cystems shyli.[29]"[14]

There are several passages in the ancient medical classics that could relate the Triple Warmer to the lymph system. Improvement in the functioning of the lymph system is one of the commonly claimed benefits of training Tai chi Chuan.

Regarding breathing and the Triple warmer, we read on page 62 of Hara Diagnosis: Reflections on the Sea "This downward movement through the Triple Warmer may well be the means by which the qi of breathing arrives below the umbilicus where it is an important ingredient in the formation of the source qi and the nourishment of the source."[15]

We all know the great emphasis placed on "sinking the ch'i" below the navel in the practice of Tai Chi Chuan. If the above theory is correct, it is the proper functioning of the Triple Warmer that allows the ch'i of breathing to reach the Tan Tien and nourish the source.

Along with the emphasis on "sinking the ch'i", Tai Chi Chuan theory emphasizes relaxation of the entire body. The Triple Warmer plays a central role in relaxation of the body due to its association with the connective tissues.

Again from Hara Diagnosis: Reflections on the Sea "The connective Tissues are an amazingly plastic, malleable, changeable, and highly functional group of tissues. That the classical Chinese authors related the triple warmer and the conduction of qi to the fascia and their connective tissues well before scientific measurement was able to demonstrate such activity is an remarkable achievement."[16]

"Oschman summarizes the basic physiological model of these structures quite elegantly: The connective tissue and fascia form a mechanical continuum, extending throughout the animal body, even into the innermost parts of each cell. All the great systems of the body -- the circulation, the nervous system, the musculo-skeletal system, the digestive tract, the various organs -- are ensheathed in connective tissue. This matrix determines the overall shape of the organism as well as the detailed architecture of its parts. All movements, of the body as a whole, or of its smallest parts, are created by tensions carried through the connective tissue fabric. Each tension, each compression, each movement causes the crystalline lattices of the connective tissues to generate bioelectric signals that are precisely characteristic of those tensions, compressions, and movements. The fabric is a semi-conducting communication network that can convey the bioelectric signals between every part of the body and every other part. This communication network within the fascia is none other than the meridian system of traditional Oriental medicine, with its countless extensions into every part of the body. As these signals flow through the tissues, their biomagnetic counterparts extend the stories they tell into the space around the body. The mechanical, bioelectric, and biomagnetic signals traveling through the connective tissue network, and through space around the body, tell the various cells how to form and reform the tissue architecture in response to the tensions, compressions, and movements we make. ⁷"[17]

These quotes show the connection of the Triple Warmer to the connective tissues and fascia of the body and reveal the depth of these tissues involvement with the other systems of the body.

Tai Chi theorizes that the tighter and more contracted a tissue becomes the less ability that tissue has to transport qi. Relaxation of the Triple Warmer is essential for the body to function at peak efficiency. For the Tai Chi Chuan practitioner it is imperative to relax the connective tissue (Triple Warmer) for proper "sinking of the ch'i", transportation of ch'i, and movement in the set.

Pericardium (Master of the Heart)

The common view of the Pericardium is that it is related to the fatty tissue surrounding the Heart but is not considered a separate organ. Its functions are to protect the Heart and act as a messenger between Shen, the ruler residing in the Heart, and the rest of the body.

Shen

Shen is often defined as spirit or mind and is the force that activates our entire being. Shen is considered to be very closely associated with the emotions.

There are two kinds of Shen. The first is the spirit we were born with. This Shen produces our general spiritual/ mental constitutional make-up.

The second kind of Shen is brought into the body after birth to nourish the original Shen. This nourished development of new Shen is accomplished through condensing the Chi of breathing in the Tan Tien.

While controlling all the functions of our being, Shen is said to reside in the Heart and communicate directly with the Kidney-Source complex.

The state of a persons Shen can be seen in his eyes. The Shen is the divine part of man that links him to the natural order of the universe.

In advanced Tai Chi Chuan the Shen of the practitioner leads the chi and jing, and catalyzes all the energetic transformations necessary to produce rejuvenation and oneness with the Tao.

"The Triple Warmer and Master of the Heart are different from the organs of the five phases. They have a more central role and greater significance because they are the precursor of all the phase, organ, and meridian relationships." [18]

From this quote we see that like the Triple Warmer, the Pericardium is a link between the source and the rest of the body. The Pericardium is yin/yang paired with the Triple Warmer which places them in a role of mutual dependency. By that pairing each is involved in the functions of the other.

On page 61 of Hara Diagnosis: Reflections on the Sea, we read; "The Master of the Heart functions energetically as a communication pathway for the shen between the heart and the "moving qi between the kidneys. 8" [19]

This function of the Pericardium is important in sinking the mind to the Tan Tien. As we shall see later, for the proper energetic transformations of Tai Chi Chuan to occur both the Chi (via the Triple Warmer) and the mind (via the Pericardium) must be able to sink to the Tan Tien.

I also believe that this function of communicating between Shen and the moving qi between the kidneys is necessary for the proper functioning of the Triple Warmer and for all higher energetic development.

Level Three

"The Shuo Wen says of the basic qi:

The basic qi divides.
The light, clear yang part becomes heaven.
The heavy, unclear yin part becomes earth." [20]

At Level Three, the yin and yang of Tai Chi -Level Two have moved thus separated. Although separate, each has a part of the other within itself. Here the various attributes of yin and yang are manifest and from their activities and interactions all other phenomena evolve.

Yin/Yang

There are already endless lists of attributes, explanations and associations connected with yin and yang and little need to present an exhaustively repetitive rendering of such lists here.

For review, yang is the active principle and is associated with fire, movement, heaven, brightness, heat, energy, expansion, etc.

Yin is the passive principle and is associated with water, stillness, earth, darkness, cold, structure, compression, etc.

All training and fighting techniques of Tai Chi Chuan and indeed all phenomena are composed of various manifestations of the principles and attributes of yin and yang.

Level Four

As we can see from the diagram, Level Four consists of a variety of phenomena begot by either the yin or yang aspect of the basic chi. For the purposes of this book we will look at the main energy systems associated with each of the yin and yang aspects.

It is interesting to note that the thirteen original postures of Tai Chi Chuan were said to represent the five elements---which are associated with the yin aspect of Level Four and the eight trigrams—which are associated with the yang aspect of level four through their relationship to the Eight Extraordinary Vessels.

This places the original thirteen postures of Tai Chi Chuan at Level Four. This is the level at which the structures of the human body are associated with the energetic systems.

Yang Aspect - Eight Extraordinary Vessels

There are Eight Extraordinary Vessels in the human body. They are closely related to the structure of the body and the balance between top and bottom, left and right, back and front, and inside and outside. Although each has its special functions they are coupled in pairs that function together as follows: Ren Mo/ Yin Chio Mo, Du Mo/Yang Chio Mo, Dai Mo/Yang Wei Mo, Chang Mo/Yin Wei Mo.

Some of the special functions of the extra meridians are as follows; they absorb excess energy from the twelve major meridians and act as resevoirs. They can release the stored energy to the other parts of the body in time of need.

The energies stored by the extraordinary vessels include; Ying, Wei, Jing, and Blood.

Ying

Ying is the nourishing, constructive energy of the body. It is said to circulate throughout the twelve major meridians. Ying comes principally from the middle warmer, being distilled during the digestive process.

"In short, Ying is at the base of what we call metabolism, for this modern term implies the structured development and sustenance of the body. [368]" [21]

Wei

Wei is considered to be the defensive energy of the body. It circulates outside the twelve major meridians especially in the skin and superficial body areas. The classics state that Wei comes from the lower burner but may authorities believe this was a misprint and that Wei originates in the upper burner.

"The Chi defensivum is responsible for the warmth of the flesh, the healthy complexion, the openness of the pores, the luster of the hair, the mobility of the joints, and as its name indicates, for the defensive capacity of the organism against every kind of heteropathy (hseih)." [22]

Jing

Jing is associated with the energy that creates the form of the human body and vitality. It is nourished by the energy produced by the digestive process. In various classical texts Jing is described as residing in the Tan Tien, Kidneys, and Ming Men. Absolute Jing, Like the Pericardium and Triple Burner is considered to have no form. The Triple Warmer along with the extraordinary vessels circulates Jing. Because Jing is associated with the energy that forms the human body and with vitality it is often related to the sexual essence. Jing energy is used in martial arts practice to manifest extraordinary powers.

Blood

Blood is both the fluid produced from food during the digestive transformations and the structural aspect of our overall configurative energy (Chi is the active aspect of configurative energy). The vital functions that blood addresses in the body depend not only on the blood being present but also on its energetic quality and its harmony with other forms of energy present.

The Eight Extra Meridians directly circulate Jing from the kidney to the rest of the body, maintain the overall blood/chi balance of the body and regulate body temperature.

They disperse Wei Chi for defending the body and Ying Chi for nourishment. Life cycles are regulated by the eight extraordinary vessels control of our endocrine glands.

The energetic transformations of Taoist meditation and Tai Chi Chuan are dependent on the Eight Extraordinary Vessels. Let us take a brief look at their individual functions and pathways as dipicted in Magnetic Healing and Meditation on Pgs 116-119[23]

Du Mo—Governing Vessel

The Du Mo controls all the Yang Meridians of the body. It flows up the center of the back and strongly influences the brain and spinal cord. This vessel circulates Jing, yang energy, and especially Wei Chi. It controls heat loss from the body and strongly influences the adrenals, reproductive organs and sympathetic nervous system.

The first half of the Taoist Microcosmic Orbit travels up the Du Mo and the second half descends via the Ren Mo. This makes these two vessels extremely important in energetic transformations within the body.

Ren Mo—Conception Vessel

Ren Mo flows along the center of the anterior part of the body. It controls all the Yin Meridians of the body. Ren Mo strongly affects the uterus, urogenital system, and the life cycles of the body. The parasympathetic nervous system is under the control of Ren Mo.

Du Mo   Ren Mo

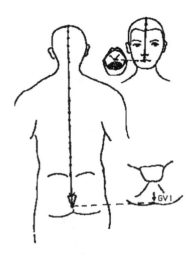
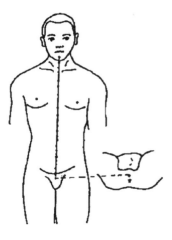

Chong Mo—Vitality Channel

Chong Mo, like Ren Mo and Du Mo originates in the Kidneys. This makes these three vessels especially closely related to the Source, "moving qi between the Kidneys", Ming Men and Tan Tien. Chong Mo plays an especially vital role in the circulation of blood and Jing. It is also called the Sea of Blood and the Sea of the Twelve Meridians due to its overall functions of providing blood and vital energy to the rest of the body.

Chong Mo removes congestions of both blood and Chi and controls all the other meridians. It directly affects the adrenal medulla, menstrual cycle, and overall body energy.

Dai Mo—Belt Channel

Dai Mo circles the waist like a belt. It is actually a group of three channels and is considered to be the only channel that runs horizontally in the body.

Although Dai Mo acts primarily on the Yang it does seek to balance energy in all the meridians that it crosses. Dai Mo connects the upper and lower parts of the body, controls the waist, and regulates energy flow to the legs. It is very closely related to the Hepato-biliary systems.

Chong Mo   Dai Mo

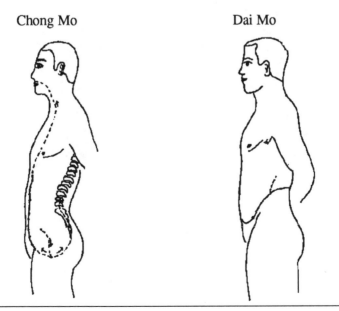

Yang Chiao Mo—Yang Heel Channel

The Yang Chiao Mo is located on the side of the body from the heel to the head. It controls the movement and balance of Yang in the body.

Yin Chiao Mo—Yin Heel Channel

The Yin Chiao Mo is located on the anterior part of the body from the inner heel area to the inner eye. It controls the movement and balance of Yin in the body.

Yang Chiao Mo   Yin Chiao Mo

Yang Wei Mo—Yang Linking Channel

Yang Wei Mo also travels between the heel and head on the lateral aspect of the body. It helps control Wei Chi and the overall body energy by linking together the various yang channels of the body.

Yin Wei Mo—Yin Linking Channel

Yin Wei Mo travels from the inner mid calf region to the throat area on the anterior body surface. This vessel links the yin channels of the body and especially acts on the Heart, blood, thyroid, and parathyroid glands.

Yang Wei Mai   Yin Wei Mai

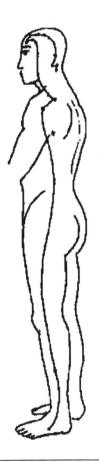 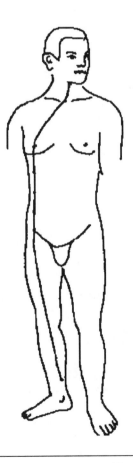

In Oriental Medicine, the Eight Extraordinary Vessels are very useful when dealing with structural problems of the body and pain along the courses of their channels as well as problems with their associated functions.

In Taoist Yoga, the Eight Extraordinary Vessels or Psychic Channels are used to facilitate the free flow of both generative fluid (Jing) and Vital Breath (Chi).

These channels are necessary for not only the circulation of generative force but also the production, discharge, and purification processes. If the Channels are not open none of these activities can take place.

The Taoists believe that all eight of the Psychic Channels are free from obstructions in the prenatal state but become obstructed after birth.

It is absolutely necessary to clear these Channels for the subtle transmutation of energetic development to take place.

The natural circulation of energy generated by the correct practice of Tai Chi Chuan is one of the very best methods to clear all the Psychic Channels and to initiate the subtle transformations of true energetic development.

Yin Aspect—Five Elements Etc.

The ancients, through their observations of nature, originated the concept of the five elements. The early references to the Five Elements in Chinese philosophy date back to before the time of Christ. Throughout the gradual development of Five Element concepts the correspondences went through numerous changes and often contradictory ideas. An early Chinese text on medical philosophy, the Nan Ching, finally correlated the diverse material into the system presently used.

The concepts of the Five Elements are used to explain interactions between things and the eternal cycle of growth and decay. Although the Five Elements are given names, i.e.: wood, fire, earth, metal, water, that suggest they represent things in reality they refer to cosmological concepts which are used to symbolically explain worldly phenomena.

The Chinese character translated as elements in this context also has the meanings of phases, movements, and crossroads all of which imply a more energetic connotation. The system is a means of grouping and organizing energetic concepts in relationship to each other into a workable whole. All phenomena can be classified as either the yin or yang aspect of one of these elements.

Five Element Correspondences[24]

	Wood	Fire	Earth	Metal	Water
Viscera	liver	heart pericardium	spleen	lung	kidney
Bowel	gall bladder	sm. intest. triple burner	stomach	large intestine	urinary bladder
Color	green	red	yellow	white	black blue
Emotion	anger	joy	reminiscence	grief sorrow	fear fright
Tissue	tendon	blood vessel	muscle	skin	bone
Sense Organ	eyes	tongue	mouth	nose	ears
Season	spring	summer	late summer	fall	winter
Taste	sour	bitter	sweet	pungent	salty
Direction	east	south	middle	west	north
Climate	wind	heat	damp	dry	cold
Nature	birth	growth	mature	harvest	store
Sound	shout	laugh	sing	weep	groan
Liquid Emitted	tears	sweat	saliva	mucous	urine
Grain	wheat	millet	rye	rice	beans
Meat	chicken	mutton	beef	horse	pork
Nourishes	nails	complexion	lips	body hair	head hair

The basic cycles of the five elements are the generating and the controlling cycles, which can be represented by the following diagram.

The Five Element Cycles[25]

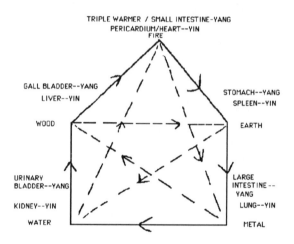

Here we see that water generates wood generates fire generates earth generates metal generates water. If this cycle were not held in check we would have unrestrained growth.

The controlling cycle balances unrestrained growth to create harmony among the five elements. In this cycle water controls fire controls metal controls wood controls earth controls water.

It is within this philosophical framework that all phenomena are inter-linked and interact. Together this system is a complete self-regulating and self generating whole.

Volumes have been written on this subject, but for our purposes a brief review of the energetic systems of the body associated with the elements will suffice. These systems are the Twelve Major Meridians and Organs.

The Twelve Major Meridians and Organs

There are six major yin organs and six major yang organs
(counting the Pericardium—yin and the Triple Burner—Yang
which are generally viewed as functions rather than physical
organs). Each organ has an associated energy channel called a
meridian which links it to the rest of the body and the cosmos.

These organ/meridians are paired (one yin with one yang),
function, and are related to the elements as follows.

Water

The Kidney (Yin) and the Urinary Bladder (Yang) are associated
with the water element. The main functions of the Kidney are to
store essential substances, dominate growth, reproduction, and
development, produce marrow, control the bones and body
fluids, manufacture blood through the marrow, and receive and
control air from the lungs. The main functions of the Urinary
Bladder are to store urine and to discharge it when the proper
amounts are in storage.

Wood

The Liver (Yin) and Gall Bladder (Yang) are associated with the
wood element. The main functions of the Liver are to store
blood, nourish the tendons, and maintain the smooth flow of
vital energy throughout the whole body, especially in the Spleen
and Stomach. The Main functions of the Gall Bladder are to
store bile and secrete it into the Small Intestine to aid digestion.

Fire

The Heart (Yin) Small Intestine (Yang) Pericardium (Yin) and
Triple Burner (Yang) are all associated with the Fire element.
The main functions of the Heart are to control the blood and
vessels and to house the mind. The Small Intestine receives
partially digested food from the Stomach, temporarily stores it
and assimilates nutrients The main functions of the Triple
Burner are the physiological functions of three areas of the
body.

The Upper Burner is the chest area and generalizes the functions of the Lungs and Heart in transporting blood and vital energy throughout the body and respiration.

The Middle Burner is the epigastric area and generalizes the functions of the Spleen and Stomach in digesting food and absorbing nutrients.

The Lower Burner is the hypogastric area and generalizes the functions of the Urinary Bladder and The Kidneys in controlling water metabolism, storing essential substances, dominating growth, reproduction and development, controlling bones, and receiving and controlling air from the Lungs. The Lower Burner is the resident place of the Source Chi.

Earth

The Spleen(Yin) and The Stomach(Yang) are associated with the Earth Element. The main functions of the Spleen are to govern digestion, absorption, and transmission of nutrients to the body, keep the blood in the vessels, hold the internal organs in place, and nourish the muscles. It is also deeply involved in water metabolism.

The main functions of the Stomach are to receive and decompose food, temporarily store the food and pass it to the Small Intestine for further digestion.

Metal

The Lungs (Yin) and Large Intestine (Yang) are associated with the Metal Element. The main functions Of the Lungs are to control respiration, regulate the water passages and nourish the skin and hair. Regulating the water passages refers to the functions of turning part of the body fluids into sweat to be excreted through the pores in the skin, controlling the pores, and energetically sending part of the body fluids down to the Kidney/Urinary Bladder complex.

The above organ descriptions were taken from Magnetic Healing and Meditation.

The following quote from Magnetic Healing and Meditation aptly describes the overall functions of this level of the energetic system. For a more detailed description of this level of the energetic system. For a more detailed description of the emotional and spirit qualities associated with the five elements refer to that book.

Life Energy [26]

A fertilized egg is the combination of life essence from the father and the mother and the infusion of Heavenly Spirit. This combination produces the basic constitutional energy upon which the physical and mental potential of the individual depends — the Source Chi. In the womb, the Source Chi is nourished by the mother. After birth its nourishment comes from the work of the organs.

The body calls upon energy from the Source Chi to aid in digestion, combat illness, and handle any emergency that requires extra life energy. The strength of the Source Chi determines the length of one's life. There is much controversy over whether Source Chi may be replaced if dissipated. Some authorities maintain that it can only be dissipated while others believe that through various means including Chi Kung (Breathing Exercises), Martial Arts and certain Oriental Medical Techniques, the Source Chi can be slowly replaced.

The body transforms food and air into life energy as follows. The food is eaten and passes to the Stomach. Here energy from the Source Chi drives off the energetic essence from the food and the Spleen directs this essence to the Lungs. In the Lungs the essence of food is mixed with the essence of the air we breathe and this mixture is acted upon by energy from the Source Chi to form Life Energy that circulates in the Meridians. This Life Energy divides into two functionally different forms, one for nourishing the body and one for protecting the body from external pathogens.

The various systems of the body use the life energy according to their needs. If there is a surplus, it is stored in the Kidneys where it can be called upon in time of need. The Kidneys use some of the stored energy to produce reproductive energy.

If the digestive system is working well, sufficient energy will be produced to meet the body's needs. If the digestive system is not working well or disease, deprivation or trauma, rob the body of energy, stored energy from the Kidneys will be used. If there is not enough energy stored in the Kidneys to meet the body's needs, Source Chi will be depleted and life shortened. Excess sexual activity will have the same effect— draining Kidney energy and shortening life.

Energy is not the only product of digested food. The grosser elements of the food(vitamins, minerals, physical nutrients, etc.) are absorbed by the gastrointestinal system to be turned into blood and other body fluids which are used to nourish and maintain the physical body. Many people believe that life energy (Vital Force) can be increased by various methods such as meditation, martial arts, or Yoga.

The basic idea here is that increasing the flow of vital force through various energy centers in the body causes the body to function more efficiently and thereby increases the production of vital energy. Some people even believe that it is possible to absorb and transform energy directly from the universe.

If we look at Chi (Energy) as the basic building block of creation and all else as but a different manifestation of this Chi, we can see the possibilities.

Energetics of the Postures

This chapter will explore the potential energetic effect of various Tai Chi Chuan postures. We will look at the energy systems activated by the Five Elements, Eight Trigrams, and the Six Phases.

Aside from the intellectual interest in this study, there may be a practical value for some people. If you knew which energy systems needed the most work to rebalance your body, extra time and attention could be spent on the postures that directly activated those systems. Also, if a particular section of the Tai Chi Chuan form was consistently more troublesome than the rest of the form, you could look for imbalances in the energy systems involved.

We have already discussed the Five Elements. The following diagram will show how they relate to the postures of Tai Chi Chuan.

Five Element Diagram

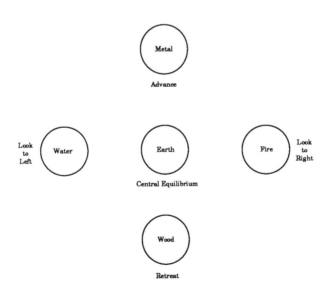

The Six Phases

The six phases are represented by the following diagram.

Six phase diagram

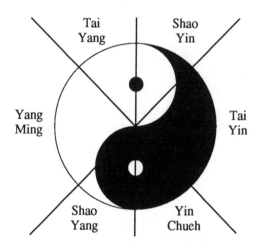

Phase	Meridians Affected
Sho Yang	Triple Warmer Gall Bladder
Yang Ming	Large Intestine Stomach
Tai Yang	Small Intestine Urinary Bladder
Shao Yin	Heart Kidney
Tai Yin	Lung Spleen
Yin Chueh	Pericardium Liver

Each phase represents a particular ratio of yin to yang in their ever changing, harmonious interplay. Each phase is associated with a particular area of the human body and the two meridians that travel through that area.

Together the six phases represent the beginning, flowering and ending domination of either yin or yang in their constant interplay.

Eight Trigrams

The Eight Trigrams are established for observing cosmic changes in the operation of the principles of the Positive Force (Yang) and the Negative Force (Yin). (Shao Kua)[2 25]

The I Ching, a collection and interpretation of a series of sixty-four six line hexagrams, is one of the first efforts of the human mind to place itself in the universe. It seems to have been prepared before 1000 BC and has exerted a living influence in China to this day. The individual hexagrams predate the I Ching.

The Chinese character for I, composed of the characters for Sun and Moon, represents change and changeless(indelability as well as easiness and clarity. The character Ching refers to a book written by a sage. These characters together intimate that nature, society, and the individual are clearly revealed through the symbols of the hexagrams.

The hexagrams describe nature in linear symbols and analyzes every phenomenon in six stages using the symbols Yin (- -) and Yang(—) to indicate the process of change. Theoretically the I Ching can trace the past, present, and future of any event no matter how complex.

From the Tai Chi symbol came the conceptual system of the I Ching. The two forms of Tai Chi led to the four symbols which lead to the Eight Trigrams.

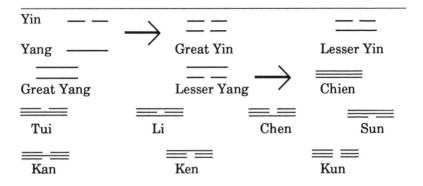

These trigrams represent the maximum number of figures that can be formed from tow kinds of lines in groups of three representing heaven, earth, and man.

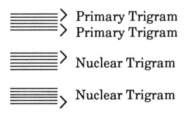

Great Yin	Lesser Yang	Lesser Yin	Great Yang
Yin		Yang	
	Tai	Chi	

Besides the two principle trigrams, each hexagram contains two nuclear trigrams:

> Primary Trigram
> Primary Trigram

Nuclear Trigram

Nuclear Trigram

From these eight trigrams the sixty-four hexagrams comprising the I Ching are formed. Each trigram has a meaning of its own and when coupled with another to become a hexagram they represent a whole developmental unit with a meaning of its own.

Each trigram has three positions corresponding to heaven (top), man (middle), and earth (bottom) with a line representing each position. The hexagrams have the same three symbolic positions but each position is represented by two lines. Within the hexagram there are two nuclear trigrams which are intimately related to both the philosophical and energetic meanings of the hexagram.

Trigrams in Tai Chi Chuan

In Tai Chi Chuan, the two sets of trigrams that form a hexagram have been translated into a series of rounded continuous movements reflecting the constant changes between Yin and Yang. These changes apply to both the visible physical body, the inner life energy, and the mind. With constant practice over a long period of time, the various aspects should join in mutual harmony on all levels bringing the full potential of the practitioner into being.

Energetically, Tai Chi Chuan can be viewed in many ways. The obvious physical movements promote overall circulation in the body and good health. The following formulation will look past the physical to the principle involved in formulating thirty-two of the positions common to most of the various branches of Tai Chi Chuan. Each of these positions is represented by a hexagram composed of two trigrams. Each trigram represents one or more energy systems in the human body. There are several theoretical correlations between energy systems in the body, the trigrams, and Tai Chi Chuan. I will discuss the three most commonly accepted representations.

First, the Five Steps, or advance, retreat, gaze to the left, gaze to the right, and central equilibrium represent the Five Elements.

Each of the elements corresponds to a set of two, or in the case of Fire, four-, paired energy systems in the body and that corresponding energy system will be affected by the step.

Metal =	Lung/Large Intestine
Water =	Kidney/Urinary Bladder
Wood =	Liver/Gall Bladder
Earth =	Spleen/Stomach
Fire =	Heart/Small Intestine
	Pericardium/Triple Warmer

There are eight methods used in performing the various postures of Tai Chi Chuan. These methods each correspond to one of the eight primary trigrams and each of the primary trigrams corresponds to both the second representation, one of the six energetic phases in Traditional Chinese medicine and the third common representation, one of the eight extraordinary meridians or energy systems in Traditional Chinese Medicine. Therefore each of these methods will activate the energy system with which it corresponds. Two of the eight trigrams represent only the extraordinary meridians.

These two trigrams are Chien and Kun which represent the extremes of Yang and Yin.

Method	Trigram	Phase	Extraordinary Meridian
1. Ward off	Chien		Du Mo
2. Pull Back	Kun		Ren Mo
3. Pull down	Sun	Yin Chueh	YinWei Mo
4. Press	Kan	Shao Yin	Dai Mo
5. Shoulder strike	Ken	Tai Yin	Yin Chiao Mo
6. Split	Chen	Shao Yang	Chong Mo
7. Push	Li	Yang Ming	Yang Wei Mo
8. Elbow	Tui	Tai Yang	Yang Chiao Mo

I have used the Tao of Tai Chi Chuan by Jou Tsung Hua[28], page 106, as my authority for corresponding the trigrams with the particular methods. Sources from different philosophical backgrounds do give other correspondences. With another set of correspondences the intellectual outcome of this study would vary but in all cases of which I am aware the same methods and trigrams are used thus the practical result would be the same energetically in that the same body systems would be activated in a different order.

Before discussing the energetic Systems most affected by the individual postures of Tai Chi Chuan, let us look at the general overall development of Chi or Life Energy brought about by correct training of Tai Chi Chuan.

Through correct training the Tai Chi Chuan practitioner learns to sink his "Chi" to the Tan Tien, a vital center in the lower abdomen. With time and practice the "Chi" will be felt to accumulate in this area and then to circulate throughout the body. At this time the practitioner can begin to use his mind to direct the "Chi". Now during practice the body will not be moved by local exertion of muscle but by the force of "Chi" directed by the mind.

As the practitioner continues to train a stage will be reached where the Chi " will be absorbed and stored in the bones. The Tan Tien eventually becomes full and overflow", allowing the accumulated "Chi" to move from the Tan Tien to the lower extremity of the spine where it generates "heat". This heat is a catalyst for the production of even more Chi which causes the soft tendons and sinews to conduct the heat through the bone sheaths and into the bones. The heated lower spinal vertebrae then "sweat" inside. As the "sweat" cools it forms a kind of marrow adhering to the inner pores of the bones. After much heating and cooling the bones will fill with this kind of marrow heralding the highest attainment of Tai Chi Chuan and the possibility of rejuvenation.

1. Beginning of Tai Chi Chuan is represented by the hexagram Chin ≡≡ ≡≡ which signifies progress. The upper trigram Li ≡≡≡≡ means sun, fire, or clinging and represents Yang Wei Mo and Yang Ming (Stomach and Large Intestine Meridians). The lower trigram Kun ≡≡ ≡≡ means earth or accepting and relates to Ren Mo. The upper nuclear trigram Kan ≡≡≡≡ means water, heart, or abysmal and represents Dai Mo and Shao Yin (Heart and Kidney Meridians). The lower nuclear trigram Ken ≡≡≡≡ means mountain or stillness and represents Yin Chiao Mo and Tai Yin (Lung and Spleen Meridians).

The Five Element representation of this posture is Earth (Central Equilibrium) representing the Stomach and Spleen Meridians.

In summary, the energetic emphasis of this posture relates to Yang Wei Mo, Ren Mo, Dai Mo, Yin Chiao Mo and the Stomach, Spleen, Large Intestine, Lung, Heart, and Kidney Meridians.

2. Grasp Birds Tail and Push Up is represented by the hexagram Chien ≣≣ which signifies the creative. In this case, all your trigrams are Chien ≣≣ which means heaven, strength, or energy, and represents Du Mo. The Five Element representations of this posture are Fire, (Heart, Small Intestine, Pericardium, Triple Warmer Meridians) and Water (Kidney and Urinary Bladder Meridians).

In summary, the energetic emphasis of this posture relates to Du Mo and the Heart, Small Intestine, Pericardium, Triple Warmer, Kidney, and Urinary Bladder Meridians.

3. Single Whip is represented by the hexagram Ko ≣≣ which signifies Revolution. The upper trigram Tui ≣≣ means joyous or lake and represents Yang Chiao Mo and Tai Yang (Urinary Bladder and Small Intestine). The lower trigram Li ≣≣ means sun, fire, or clinging and represents Yang Wei Mo and Yang Ming (Stomach and Large Intestine). The upper nuclear trigram Chien ≣≣ means heaven, strength, and energy and represents Du Mo. The lower nuclear trigram Sun ≣≣ means gentle or wind and represents Yin Wei Mo and Yin Chueh (Pericardium and Liver Meridians). The Fire element representation of the posture is Water (Kidney, Urinary Bladder Meridians).

In summary, the energetic emphasis of this posture

relates to Yang Chiao Mo, Yang Wie Mo, Du Mo, Yin Wie Mo, and the Urinary Bladder, Small Intestine, Stomach, Large Intestine, Liver, and Pericardium Meridians.

4. Play Guitar is represented by the hexagram Sui ☳ which denotes following.

The upper trigram Tui ☱ means joyous or lake and represents Yang Chiao Mo and Tai Yang (Urinary Bladder and Small Intestine Meridians). The lower trigram Chen ☳ means arousing or thunder and relates to Ching Mo and Shao Yang (Triple Warmer and Gall Bladder Meridians). The upper nuclear trigram Sun ☴ means gentle or wind and relates to Yin Wei Mo and Yin Chueh (Liver and Pericardium Meridians). The lower nuclear trigram Ken ☶ means mountain or stillness and relates to Yin Chiao Mo and Tai Yin (Lung and Spleen Meridians). The Five Element representation of this posture is Fire (Heart, Small Intestine, Pericardium, Triple Warmer Meridians).

In summary, the energetic emphasis of the posture relates to Yang Chiao Mo, Chong Mo, Yin Wei Mo, and the Urinary Bladder, Small Intestine, Gall Bladder, Triple Warmer, Liver, Pericardium, Ling, and Spleen Meridians

5. Step Forward and Strike with Shoulder is represented by the hexagram Ta Chuang ☳ which symbolizes the power of the great. The upper trigram Chen ☳ means arousing or thunder and relates to Chong Mo and Shao Yang (Triple Warmer and Gall Bladder). The lower trigram Chien ☰ means heaven, strength, energy, or to turn and relates to Du Mo. The upper nuclear trigram Tui ☱ means joyous, or lake and relates to Yang Chiao Mo and Tai Yang (Urinary Bladder and Small Intestine Meridians). The lower nuclear trigram Chien means heaven, strength, energy, or to turn and relates to Du Mo. The Five Element representation of this position is metal (Lung, Large Intestine Meridians).

In summary, the energetic emphasis of this posture relates to Chong Mo, Du Mo, Yang Chiao Mo, and the Triple Warmer, Gall Bladder, Urinary Bladder, Small Intestine, Lung, and Large Intestine Meridians.

6. White Crane Spreads its Wings is represented by the hexagram Pi ䷔ which means grace or beauty of form. The upper trigram Ken ☶ means mountain or stillness and relates to Yin Chiao Mo and Tai Yin (Lung and Spleen Meridians). The lower trigram Li ☲ means sun, fire or clinging, and relates to Yang Wei Mo and Yang Ming (Stomach and Large Intestine Meridians). The upper nuclear trigram Chen ☳ means arousing or thunder and relates to Chong Mo and Shao Yang (Gall Bladder and Triple Warmer Meridians). The lower nuclear trigram Kan ☵ means water, heart, or abysmal and relates to Dai Mo and Shao Yin (Kidney and Heart Meridians). The Five Element representation of this posture is earth and relates to the Stomach and Spleen Meridians.

In summary, the energetic emphasis of this posture relates to Yin Chiao Mo, Yang Wei Mo, Chong Mo, Dai Mo, and the Lung, Spleen, Stomach, Large Intestine, Urinary Bladder, Triple Warmer, Kidney, and Heart Meridians.

7. Brush Knee and Push is represented by the hexagram Ku ䷑ which signifies decay or to work on what was spoiled to remove the source of decay. The upper trigram Ken ☶ means mountain or stillness and relates to Yin Chiao Mo and Tai Yin (Spleen and Lung Meridians). The lower trigram Sun ☴ means gentle of wind and relates to Yin Wei Mo and Yin Chueh (Liver and Pericardium Meridians). The upper nuclear trigram Chen ☳ means arousing, or thunder and relates to Chong Mo and Sao Yang (Gall Bladder and Triple Warmer Meridians). The lower nuclear trigram Tui ☱ means joyous or lake and relates to Yang Chiao Mo and Tai Yang (Urinary Bladder and Small Intestine Meridians).

The Five Element representations of this posture are metal (Lung and Large Intestine Meridians), and fire (Heart, Small Intestine, Triple Warmer, and Pericardium Meridians).

In summary, the energetic emphasis of this posture relates to Yin Chiao Mo, Yin Wei Mo, Chong Mo, Yang Chiao Mo, and the Spleen, Lung, Liver, Pericardium, Gall Bladder, Triple Warmer, Urinary Bladder, Small Intestine, and Large Intestine Meridians.

8. Step Forward and punch is represented by the hexagram Yu ☳☷ which denotes enthusiasm. The upper trigram Chen ☳ means arousing or thunder and Shao Yang (Gall Bladder and Triple Warmer Meridians). The lower trigram Kun ☷ means earth or accepting and relates to Ren Mo. The upper nuclear trigram Kan ☵ means water, heart, or abysmal and relates to Dai Mo and and Shao Yin (Heart and Kidney Meridians). The lower nuclear trigram Ken ☶ means mountain or stillness and relates to Yin Chiao Mo and Tai Yin (Lung and Spleen Meridians). The Five Element representation of this postureis Metal (Lung and Large Intestine Meridians).

In summary, the energetic emphasis of this posture relates to Chong Mo, Ren Mo, Dai Mo, Yin Chiao Mo, and the Gall Bladder, Triple Warmer, Heart, Kidney, Lung, Spleen, and Large Intestine Meridians.

9. Cross Hands is represented by the hexagram Ming ☷☲ which means the darkening of the light. The upper trigram Kun ☷ means earth or accepting and relates to Ren Mo. The lower trigram Li ☲ means sun, fire, or clinging and relates to Yang Wei Mo and Yang Ming (Stomach and Large Intestine Meridians). The upper nuclear trigram Chen ☳ means arousing or thunder and relates to Chong Mo and Shao Yang (Triple Warmer and Gall Bladder Meridians). The lower nuclear trigram

Kan ☵ means water, heart, or abysmal and relates to Dai Mo and Shao Yin (Kidney and Heart Meridians). The Five Element representation of the posture is Metal (Lung, and Large Intestine Meridians).

In summary, the energetic emphasis of this posture relates to Ren Mo, Yin Wei Mo, Chong Mo, Dai Mo, and the Stomach, Large Intestine, Triple Warmer, Gall Bladder, Kidney, Heart, and Lung Meridians.

10. Bring Tiger to the Mountain is represented by the hexagram Ken ☶ which means stillness or mountain. Both the upper and lower trigram are Ken ☶ which means mountain or stillness and relates to Yin Chiao and Tai Yin (Lung and Spleen Meridians). The upper nuclear trigram Chen ☳ means arousing, or thunder and relates to Chong Mo and Shao Yang (Triple Warmer and Gall Bladder Meridians). The lower nuclear trigram Kan ☵ means water,heart or abysmal and relates to Dai Mo and and Shao Yin (Heart and Kidney Meridians). The Five Element representations of this posture are Fire (Heart, Small Intestine, Pericardium, Triple Warmer, and Metal (Lung and Large Intestine Meridians).

In summary, the energetic emphasis of this posture relates to Yin Chiao Mo, Chong Mo, Dai Mo, and the Lung, Spleen, Triple Warmer, Gall Bladder, Heart, Kidney, Small Intestine, Pericardium, and Large Intestine Meridians.

11. Fist Under the Elbow is represented by the hexagram I ☶ which denotes the corners of the mouth or providing nourishment. The upper trigram Ken ☶ means mountain or stillness and relates to Yin Chiao Mo and Tai Yin (Lung and Spleen Meridians). The lower trigram Chen ☳ means arousing or thunder and relates to Chong Mo and Shao Yang (Triple Warmer and

Gall Bladder, Meridians). Both the upper and lower nuclear trigrams are Kun ☷ ☷ meaning earth or accepting and relate to Ren Mo. The Five Element representation of this form is Wood (Liver and Gall Bladder Meridians).

In summary, the energetic emphasis of this posture relates to Yin Chiao Mo, Chong Mo, Ren Mo, and the Lung, Spleen, Gall Bladder, Triple Warmer, and Liver Meridians.

12. Step Back and Repulse Monkey is represented by the hexagram Tun ☰☶ meaning retreat. The upper trigram Chien ☰ means heaven, strength, energy, or to turn and relates to Du Mo. The lower trigram Li ☲ means sun, fire, or clinging and relates to Yang Wei Mo and Yang Ming (Large Intestine and Stomach Meridians). The upper nuclear trigram Chien ☰ is identical to the upper trigram. The lower nuclear trigram Sun ☴ means gentle or wind and relates to Yin Wei Mo and Yin Chueh (Pericardium and Liver Meridian). The Five Element representation of this posture is wood (Lung and Large Intestine Meridian).

In summary, the energetic emphasis of this posture relates to Du Mo, Yang Wei Mo, Yin Wei Mo and the Large Intestine, Stomach, Liver, Pericardium and Lung Meridians.

13. Slant Flying is represented by the hexagram Huan ☴☵ which means dissolution. The upper trigram Sun ☴ means gentle or wind and relates to Yin Wei Mo and Yin Chueh (Liver and Pericardium). The lower trigram Kan ☵ means water, heat, or abysmal and relates to Dai Mo and Shao Yin (Heart and Kidney Meridians). The upper nuclear trigram Ken ☶ means mountain or stillness and relates to Yin Chiao Mo and Tai Yin (Lung and Spleen Meridians. The

lower nuclear trigram Chen ⚏ means arousing or thunder and relates to Chong Mo and Shao Yang (Triple Warmer and Gall Bladder Meridians). The Five Element representation of this posture is Metal (Lung and Large Intestine Meridians) and Fire (Heart, Pericardium. Small Intestine, and Triple Warmer Meridians).

In summary, the energetic emphasis of this posture relates to Yin Wei Mo, Dai Mo, Yin Chiao Mo, Chong Mo, and the Liver, Pericardium, Heart, Kidney, Lung, Spleen, Triple Warmer, Gall Bladder and Small Intestine Meridians.

14. Needle at the Sea Bottom is represented by the hexagram Hsiao Kuo ䷽ which means preponderance of the small. The upper trigram Chen ⚏ means arousing or thunder and relates to Chong Mo and Shao Yang (Triple Warmer and Gall Bladder Meridians). The lower trigram Ken ⚍ means mountain or stillness and relates to Yin Chiao Mo and Tai Yin (Lung and Spleen Meridians). The upper nuclear trigram Tui ⚌ means lake or joyous and relates to Yang Chiao Mo and Tai Yang (Urinary Bladder and Small Intestine Meridians). The lower nuclear trigram Sun ⚎ means gentle or wind and relates to Yin Wei Mo and Yin Chueh (Liver and Pericardium Meridians). The Five Element representation of this posture is Metal (Large Intestine and Lung Meridians).

In summary, the energetic emphasis of this posture relates to Chong Mo, Yin Chiao Mo, Yang Chiao Mo, Yin Wei Mo and the Gall Bladder, Triple Warmer, Lung, Spleen, Urinary Bladder, Small Intestine. Liver, Pericardium, and Large Intestine Meridians.

15. Play Arms Like a Fan is represented by the hexagram Ta Ch'u ䷙ meaning taming power of the great. The upper trigram Ken ⚍ means mountain or stillness

and relates to Yin Chiao Mo and Tai Yin (Lung and Spleen Meridians). The lower trigram Chien ═══ ═══ means heaven, strength, or energy and relates to Du Mo. The upper nuclear trigram Chen ═══ ═══ means arousing or thunder and relates to Chong Mo and Shao Yang (Triple Warmer and Gall Bladder Meridians). The lower nuclear trigram Tui ═══ ═══ means joyous or lake and relates to Yang Chiao Mo and Tai Yang (Urinary Bladder and Small Intestine Meridians). The Five Element representation of the posture is Metal (Lung, and Large Intestine Meridians).

In summary, the energetic emphasis of this posture is Yin Chiao Mo, Du Mo, Chong Mo, Yang Chiao Mo, and the Lung, Spleen, Gall Bladder, Triple Warmer, Urinary Bladder, Small Intestine and Large Intestine Meridians.

16. Turn Body and Strike Fist to Back is represented by the hexagram Ta Kuo ═══ ═══ which means preponderance of the great. The upper trigram Tui ═══ ═══ means joyous or lake and represents Yang Chiao Mo and Tai Yang (Urinary Bladder and Small Intestine Meridians). The lower trigram Sun ═══ ═══ means gentle or wind and represents Yin Wei Mo and Yin Chueh (Liver and Pericardium Meridians). Both the upper and lower nuclear trigrams are Chien ═══ ═══ which means heaven, strength, energy, and to turn and represent Du Mo. The Five Element representation of this posture is Fire (Heart, Pericardium, Triple Warmer, Small Intestine Meridians).

In summary, the energetic emphasis of this posture is Yang Chiao Mo, Du Mo, Yin Wei Mo and the Small Intestine, Urinary Bladder, Liver, Pericardium, Heart, and Triple Warmer Meridians.

17. Hit Tiger is represented by the hexagram I ═══ ═══ which signifies increase. The upper trigram Sun ═══ ═══ means gentle of wind and relates to Yin Wei Mo and Yin Chueh

(Liver and Pericardium Meridians). The lower trigram Chen ☳ means arousing and thunder and relates to Chong Mo and Shao Yang (Triple Warmer and Gall Bladder Meridians). The upper nuclear trigrams Ken ☶ means mountain or stillness and relates to Yin Chiao Mo and Tai Yin (Lung and Spleen Meridians). The lower nuclear trigram Kun ☷ means earth or accepting and relates to Ren Mo. The Five Element representation of this posture is Metal (Lung and Large Intestine Meridians) and Wood (Liver and Gall Bladder Meridians).

In summary, the energetic emphasis of this posture is Yin Wei Mo, Chong Mo, Yin Chiao Mo, Ren Mo, and the Liver, Pericardium, Triple Warmer, Gall Bladder, Lung, Spleen, and Large Intestine Meridians.

18. Kick with Toes is represented by the hexagram Meng ䷃ which means youthful folly. The upper trigram Ken ☶ means mountain or stillness and relates to Yin Chiao Mo and Tai Yin (Lung and Spleen Meridians). The lower trigram Kan ☵ means water, heart, or abysmal and relates to Dai Mo and Shao Yin (Heart and Kidney Meridians). The upper nuclear trigram Kun ☷ means earth or accepting and relates to Ren Mo. The lower nuclear trigram Chen ☳ means arousing and thunder and relates to Chong Mo and Shao Yang (Gall Bladder and Triple Warmer Meridians). The Five Element representation of this posture is Earth (Stomach and Spleen Meridians).

In summary, the energetic emphasis of this posture are Yin Chiao Mo, Dai Mo, Ren Mo, Chong Mo, and the Lung, Spleen, Heart, Kidney, Gall Bladder, Triple Warmer, and Stomach Meridians.

19. Hit Opponents Ears with Fists is represented by the hexagram Shih Ho ䷔ which means biting through. The upper trigram Li ☲ means sun, fire, or clinging

and relates to Yang Wei Mo and Yang Ming (Stomach and
Large Intestine Meridians). The lower trigram
Chen ☳ means arousing or thunder and relates to
Chong Mo andShao Yang (Gall Bladder and Triple Burner).
The upper nuclear trigram Kan ☵ means water,
heart, or abysmal and relates to Dai Mo and Shao Yin (Heart
and Kidney Meridian). The lower nuclear trigram
Ken ☶ means mountain or stillnessand relates to Yin
Chiao Mo and Tai Yin (Spleen and Lung Meridian). The Five
Element representation of this posture is Metal (Lung and
Large Intestine Meridians).

In summary, the energetic emphasis of this posture are Yang
Wei Mo, Chong Mo, Dai Mo, Yin Chiao Mo, and the Gall
Bladder, Triple Warmer, Stomach, Large Intestine, Heart,
Kidney, Spleen, and Lung Meridians.

20. Turn Body and Kick is represented by the hexagram Wu
Wang ☰☳ meaning innocence. The upper trigram
Chien ☰ means heaven, strength, energy, and to turn
and relates to Du Mo. The lower trigram Chen ☳
means arousing or thunder and relates to Chong Mo and
Shao Yang (Gall Bladder and Triple Warmer Meridians).
The upper nuclear trigram Sun ☴ means gentle or
wind and relates to Yin Wei Mo and Yin Chueh (Liver and
Pericardium Meridians). The lower nuclear trigram
Ken ☶ means mountain or stillness and relates to Yin
Chiao Mo and Tai Yin (Lung and Spleen Meridians). The
Five Element representation of this posture is Water
(Kidney and Urinary Bladder Meridians).

In summary, the energetic emphasis of this posture are Du
Mo, Chong Mo, Yin Wei Mo, Yin Chiao Mo, and the Gall
Bladder, Triple Warmer, Liver, Pericardium, Lung, Spleen,
Kidney, and Urinary Bladder Meridians.

21. Wave Hands Like a Cloud is represented by the hexagram
Chun ☵☳ which means difficulty at the beginning. The

upper trigram Kan ≡≡ ≡≡ means water, heat, abysmal and relates to Dai Mo and Shao Yin (Kidney and Heart Meridians). The lower trigram Chen ≡≡ ≡≡ means arousing and thunder and relates to Chong Mo and Shao Yang (Gall Bladder and Triple Warmer Meridians). The upper nuclear trigram Ken ≡≡ ≡≡ means mountain or stillness and relates to Yin Chiao Mo and Tai Yin (Lung and Spleen Meridians). The lower nuclear trigram Kun ≡≡ ≡≡ means earth or accepting and relates to Ren Mo. The Five Element representation of this posture is Fire (Heart, Pericardium, Small Intestine, and Triple Warmer), and Water (Kidney and Urinary Bladder Meridians).

In summary, the energetic emphasis of this posture are Dai Mo, Chong Mo, Yin Chiao Mo, Ren Mo, and the Kidney, Heart, Gall Bladder, Triple 'Warmer, Lung, Spleen, Pericardium, Urinary Bladder, and Small Intestine Meridians.

22. Snake Creeps Down is represented by the hexagram Shih ≡≡ ≡≡ which means army. Both the upper trigram and the upper nuclear trigram are Kun ≡≡ ≡≡ which means earth or accepting and relates to Ren Mo. The lower trigram is Kan ≡≡ ≡≡ which means heart, water, or abysmal and relates to Dai Mo and Shao Yin (Heart and Kidney Meridians). The lower nuclear trigram Chen ≡≡ ≡≡ means arousing or thunder and relates to Chong Mo and Shao Yang (Triple Warmer and Gall Bladder Meridians). The Five Element representation of this posture is Earth (Stomach and Spleen Meridians).

In summary, the energetic emphasis of this posture are Ren Mo, Dai Mo, Chong Mo, and the Heart, Kidney, Triple Warmer, Gall Bladder, Stomach, and Spleen Meridians.

23. Golden Cock Stands on One Leg is represented by the hexagram Chung Fu ≡≡ ≡≡ which means inner truth. The upper trigram Sun ≡≡≡ means gentle or wind and

relates to Yin Wei Mo and Yin Chueh (Liver and
Pericardium Meridians). The lower trigram Tui ☱
means lake or joyous and relates to Yang Chiao Mo and Tai
Yang (Urinary Bladder and Small Intestine Meridians). The
upper nuclear trigram Ken ☶ means mountain or
stillness and relates to Yin Chiao Mo and Tai Yin (Lung and
Spleen Meridians). The lower nuclear trigram Chen ☳
means thunder or arousing and relates to Chong Mo and
Shao Yang (Triple Warmer and Gall Bladder Meridians).
The Five Element representation of this posture is Earth
(Stomach and Spleen Meridians).

In summary, the energetic emphasis of this posture are Yin
Wei Mo, Yang Chiao Mo, Yin Chiao, Chong Mo, and the
Liver, Pericardium, Small Intestine, Urinary Bladder, Lung,
Spleen, Triple Warmer, Gall Bladder, and Stomach
Meridians.

24 High Pat on Horse is represented by the hexagram
Lu ䷷ which means the wanderer. The upper trigram
Li ☲ means sun, fire, clinging, relates to Yang Wei Mo
and Yang Ming (Stomach and Large Intestine Meridians).
The lower trigram Ken ☶ means mountain or stillness
and relates to Yin Chiao Mo and Tai Yin (Lung and Spleen
Meridians). The upper nuclear trigram Tui ☱ means
lake or joyous and relates to Yang Chiao Mo and Tai Yang
(Urinary Bladder and Small Intestine Meridians). The lower
nuclear trigram Sun ☴ means gentle or wind and
relates to Yin Wei Mo and Yin Chueh (Liver and
Pericardium Meridians). The Five Element representation
of this posture is Wood (Liver,and Gall Bladder Meridians).

In summary, the energetic emphasis of this posture are Yang
Wei Mo, Yin Chiao Mo, Yang Chiao Mo, Yin Wei Mo, and the
Stomach, Large Intestine, Lung, Spleen, Urinary Bladder,
Small Intestine, Liver, Pericardium, and Gall Bladder
Meridians.

25. Separate Feet and Kick is represented by the hexagram Chen which ☳☳ means the arousing or thunder. Both the upper and lower trigrams are Chen ☳ ☳ which means the arousing or thunder and relates to Chong Mo and Shao Yang (Gall Bladder and Triple Warmer Meridians. The upper nuclear trigram Kan ☵ means water, heart, or abysmal and relates to Dai Mo and Shao Yin (Heart and Kidney Meridians). The lower nuclear trigram Ken ☶ means mountain or stillness and relates to Yin Chiao Mo and Tai Yin (Lung and Spleen Meridians). The Five Element representation of this posture is Earth (Stomach and Spleen Meridians).

In summary, the energetic emphasis of this posture are Chong Mo, Dai Mo, Yin Chiao Mo, and the Gall Bladder, Triple Warmer, Heart, Kidney, Lung. Spleen. and Stomach Meridians.

26. Step Forward and Punch to Opponents Lower Abdomen is represented by the hexagram Chien ☶☷ which means modesty. The upper trigram is Kun ☷ ☷ which means earth and accepting and relates to Ren Mo. The lower trigram is Ken ☶ which means mountain or stillness and relates to Yin Chiao Tai Yin (Lung and Spleen Meridians). The upper nuclear trigram Chen ☳ means arousing or thunder and relates to Chong Mo and Shao Yang (Gall Bladder and Triple Warmer Meridians). The lower nuclear trigram Kan ☵ means heart, water, or abysmal and relates to Dai Mo and Shao Yin (Heart and Kidney Meridians). The Five Element representation of this posture is Metal (Lung and Large Intestine Meridians).

In summary the energetic emphasis of this posture are Ren Mo, Yin Chiao Mo, Chong Mo, Dai Mo and the Lung, Spleen, Gall Bladder, Triple Warmer, Heart, Kidney, and Large Intestine Meridians.

27. Fair Lady Works at Shuttle is represented by
Chieh ䷻ which signifies limitation. The upper trigram
Kan ☵ means water, heart or abysmal and relates to
Dai Mo and Shao Yin (Kidney and Heart Meridians). The
lower trigram Tui ☱ means lake or joyous and relates
to Yang Chiao and Tai Yang (Urinary Bladder and Small
Intestine Meridians). The upper nuclear trigram
Ken ☶ means mountain or stillness and relates to Yin
Chiao Mo and Tai Yin (Lung and Spleen Meridians). The
lower nuclear trigram Chen ☳ means arousing and
thunder and relates to Chong Mo and Shao Yang (Triple
Warmer and Gall Bladder Meridians). The Five Element
representations of this posture are Water (Kidney and
Urinary Bladder Meridians) and Fire (Heart, Triple
Warmer, Small Intestine, and Pericardium Meridians).

In summary, the energetic emphasis of this posture are Dai
Mo, Yang Chiao Mo, Yin Chiao, Chong Mo and the Kidney,
Heart, Urinary Bladder, Small Intestine, Lung, Spleen,
Triple Warmer, Gall Bladder, and Pericardium Meridians.

28. Step Forward, Seven Stars is represented by the hexagram
Feng ䷶ denoting abundance. The upper trigram
Chen ☳ means arousing or thunder and relates to
Chong lo and Shao Yang (Gall Bladder and Triple Warmer
Meridians). The lower trigram Li ☲ means sun, fire,
or clinging and relates to Yang Wei and Yang Ming
(Stomach and Large Intestine Meridians). The upper nuclear
trigram Tui ☱ means lake or joyous and relates to
Yang Chiao Mo and Tai Yang (Urinary Bladder .and Small
Intestine Meridians). The lower nuclear trigram
Sun ☴ means gentle or wind and relates to Yin Wei
Mo and Yin Chueh (Liver and Pericardium Meridians!s).
The Five Element representation of this posture is Metal
(Lung and Large Intestine Meridians).

In summary, the energetic emphasis of this posture are
Chong Mo, Yang Wei Mo, Yang Chiao Mo Yin Wei Mo, and
the Gall Bladder, Triple Warmer, Stomach, Large Intestine,

Urinary ladder, Small Intestine, Liver, Pericardium, and Lung Meridians.

29. Ride Tiger to the Mountain is represented by the hexagram Chien ☰☷ which means development. The upper trigram Sun ☴ means gentle or wind and relates to Yin Wei Mo and Yin Chueh (Pericardium or Liver Meridians)The lower trigram Ken ☶ means mountain or stillness and relates to Yin Chiao Mo and Tai Yin (Lung and Spleen Meridians). The upper nuclear trigram Li ☲ means sun, fire, or clinging and relates to Yong Wei Mo and Yang Ming (Stomach and Large Intestine Meridians). The lower nuclear trigrams Kan ☵ means water, heart, or abysmal and relates to Dai Mo and Shao Yin (Kidney and Heart Meridians). The Five Element representation of this posture is Wood (Liver and Gall Bladder Meridians).

In summary, the energetic emphasis of this posture are Yin Wei Mo, Yang Wei Mo, Yin Chiao Mo, Dai Mo, and the Pericardium, Liver, Lung, Spleen, Large Intestine, Stomach, Kidney, and Heart Meridians.

30. Turn Body and do Lotus Kick is represented by the hexagram Wei Chi ☲☵ which means before completion. The upper trigram and the lower nuclear trigram are Li ☲ which means sun, fire, or clinging and relates to Yang Wei Mo and Yang Ming (Stomach and Large Intestine meridians). The lower trigram and the upper nuclear trigram Kan ☵ means water, heart, abysmal and relates to Dai Mo and Shao Yin (Heart and Kidney Meridians). The Five Element representation of this posture is Fire (Heart, Small Intesstine, Pericardium, and Triple Warmer Meridians).

In summary, the energetic emphasis of this posture are Yang Wei Mo, Dai Mo, and the Stomach, Large Intestine, Heart, Kidney, Pericardium, Triple Warmer, and Small Intestine Meridians.

31. Shoot Tiger is represented by the hexagram Hsieh ☰☰ meaning deliverance. The upper trigram Chen ☰☰ means arousing and thunder and relates to Chong Mo and Shao Yang (Gall Bladder and Triple Warmer Meridians). The lower trigram and upper nuclear trigram are Kan ☰☰ which means water, heat, and abysmal and relates to Dai Mo and Shao Yin (Heart and Kidney Meridians). The lower nuclear trigram Li ☰☰ means sun, fire, or clinging and relates to Yang Wei Mo and Yang Ming (Large Intestine and Stomach Meridians). The Five Element representation of this posture is Metal (Lung and Large Intestine Meridians).

In summary, the energetic emphasis of this posture are Chong Mo, Dai Mo, Yang 'Wei Mo, and the Gall Bladder, Triple Warmer, Heart, Kidney, Large Intestine, Stomach, and Lung Meridians.

32. Circle Fist is represented by the hexagram Ting which means the cauldron. The upper trigram Ting Li ☰☰ means sun, fire, or clinging and relates to Yang Wei Mo and Yang Ming (Large Intestine and Stomach Meridians). The lower trigram Sun ☰☰ means gentle or wind and relates to Yin Wei Mo and Yin Chueh (Pericardium and Liver Meridians). The upper nuclear trigram Tui ☰☰ means lake or joyous and relates to Yang Chiao Mo and Tai Yang (Urinary Bladder and Small Intestine Meridians). The lower nuclear trigram Chien ☰☰ means heaven, strength, or energy relates to Du Mo. The Five Element representation of this posture is Earth (Stomach and Spleen Meridians).

In summary the energetic emphasis of this posture are Yang Wei Mo, Yin Wei Mo, Yang Chiao Mo, Du Mo, and the Large Intestine, Stomach, Liver, Pericardium, Urinary Bladder, Small Intestine, and Spleen Meridians. [29]

In conclusion, the above theoretical formulation of the energetics of Tai Chi Chuan postures must be viewed with an overall understanding of the purpose of Tai Chi Chuan. That purpose is to totally open the body for the continuous unkindred flow of vital energy. Ideally each posture would then initiate a flow in all the channels throughout the body. The development of this open flow would take quite sometime to achieve and until that ideal were reached each posture would in fact affect various channels more than others. The affected channels philosophically would be those that had a direct correspondence to the various trigrams contained in the hexagrams from which the idea for that posture emerged.

The Form

Several different styles of Tai Chi Chuan have evolved through the years. Even within the same styles, different forms have evolved. Since Tai Chi Chuan aims at developing ones own nature it should be expected that students learning from the same teacher would manifest the teachings in a manner unique to themselves. The uniqueness of the individual, his background and time spent in training, and the depth of his understanding on both the intellectual and experiential levels all contribute to the variety of forms circulating in the Tai Chi Chuan community.

The most important factor in determining the value of a specific form is its adherence to the principles expressed in the Tai Chi Chuan Classics.

The form itself is a tool for development, not an end in itself. The concentration, awareness, control, discipline and eventual abandonment of the intellect expressed through and demanded by the form at various levels of development provide the practitioner with the necessary circumstances for development. It is up to the practitioner to take full advantage of these circumstances for his own progress.

The constantly changing energetic environment provided by the correct training of the form will present the practitioner with endless challenges to change and progress. If he fails to meet these challenges, his progress will stagnate. It is not unusual to find twenty year veterans of Tai Chi Chuan Training with little energetic development. Progress takes much more than wandering through the set once a day for a certain number of years. Diligence and hard work on all levels are required for the real energetic transformations that result in development to take place.

Training the form

In the beginning years of training a great deal of practice and attention is needed just to understand the physical aspects of

Tai Chi Chuan. Since the form itself is the basic tool of this path it is necessary to put a great deal of study into this aspect of the art.

Assuming you train consistently and progress, the physical manifestation as well as the energetic environment within the form will change throughout your years of practice. In a very great sense there is no "correct" form but there are correct principles that must be attentively applied to the best of your ability at the level you have reached.

This attentive application requirement is one of the great challenges inherent in Tai Chi Chuan. It is very difficult to maintain the necessary attention to detail required for progress on a training schedule that encompasses not only days, weeks and years but hopefully the rest of your life.

Progress through the form will range from grossly attempting to hold your body in the perceived correct posture to not only being able to do the energetic form without moving the body but to actually being able to train your spirit and energy outside the physical body.

Principles

The three most important principles to explore as a beginning student are sinking, moving together, and relaxing. These principles will in time and with proper training permeate the many levels of our energetic being and catalyze the most profound energetic transformations.

As with any part of our energetic being and the art of Tai Chi Chuan, it is impossible to speak of one aspect by itself. All parts of ourselves and our art are holistically interconnected. Trying to separate any part for our intellects to grasp runs the same risks as trying to grasp the intellectual correct posture— stagnation and narrow superficiality.

For an intellectual exercise such as this book, it is necessary to separate various aspects of our subject for discussion, but always keep in mind the holistic view.

Sinking

Sinking itself has three important aspects: sinking the mind (Spirit) to the Tan Tien, sinking the chi to the Tan Tien, and sinking the vital energy to the feet (rooting).

The three aspects of sinking can be trained within the Tai Chi Chuan form, but also necessitate supplementary training outside the form.

Training the sinking of the mind and the chi to the Tan Tien can be accomplished through meditation and chi gung (breathing exercises).

Chi Gung practices are also useful for sinking the root to the feet.

"of thousands of changes, none is unrelated with the root." Here the work "root" denotes the "foot" as well as the center of gravity." [30]

The best, and I think, an absolutely necessary exercise for developing the root is some form of stance training or standing meditation.

Stance training can be accomplished through utilizing various postures from the Tai Chi Chuan form, various individual stance exercises or any one of the many standing meditation forms.

In my style, it takes a minimum of three years of practicing stance exercises one hour a day to develop the bare beginnings of a root. From that point the root may be further developed through the form. It is like the old saying,'It takes money to make money." Without a root to train in the form it is difficult to further develop it.

"As the classics say, "if the yung Ch'uan (bubbling well) has no root and the waist has no commander, studying hard till death will be of no help." [31] The Yug Ch'un is on acupuncture point on the bottom of the foot otherwise known as Kidney. The comander in the waist is the mind sinking to the Tan Tein.

The stronger the root, the more the energy will move within the form and the more rapidly one will develop.

Root is much more than strong leg muscles. It is the literal sinking of the source chi to the ground. This cannot be accomplished by running, weight lifting, swimming, or any of the usual leg strengthening exercises of the west, including dancing.

When stance work is done correctly, the body is held in such a position that the energy is encouraged to center in the Tan Tien and flow to the feet. Opening these pathways to the free flow of energy requires a good deal of time and patience, but their opening is the key to higher development.

Many practitioners believe one of the key differences between the great masters of the past and present practitioners is the amount of time spent in stance training.

In many of the histories of very developed masters of the past we notice a heavy emphasis on stance work. For example, it is stated on page 21 of Tai Chi Ch'uan Ta Wen that "Yang Lu-Ch'an, in Squatting Single Whip could pick up a coin from the ground with his month. Moreover, his waist was so flexible that he could use his shoulder against an opponents knee."[32]

We have already seen that the Shen-mind-spirit communicates with the source-Tan Tien- Ming Men- through one of the functions of the Pericardium. This communication or sinking is vital for balanced development and energetic transformation. It is possible to partially sink the chi to the Tan Tien without the balance of the mind. This sinking of the chi can generate large amounts of energy but without the Shen to influence this energy with spirit/intelligence imbalances and inefficiencies can develop.

Sinking the mind-Shen-Spirit to the Tan Tien means much more than simply thinking of the area below the navel. When the mind truly reaches the Tan Tien we think not of but through that area. The chi is mobilized by the mind thinking through the Tan Tien. "It is important to be completely in the mind (heart) and waist, and not outside."[33]

Sinking the mind to the Tan Tien can carry over from the practices of Tai Chi Chuan to everyday life. This phenomenon puts the practitioner in a whole new experiential world. The everyday routines of life take on a whole new interest and offer constant opportunities for higher energetic training.

Sinking the Chi to the Tan Tien involves utilizing the internal channel of the Triple Burner to bring chi from the air we breath to the area below the navel. As we have already seen the source chi can be nourished via this pathway. When the chi from the air we breath reaches the Tan Tien it not only nourishes the source, but also interacts with the jing stored there. This interaction produces Shen. So both the Pericardium and the Triple Warmer influence Shen in the Tan Tien; the Pericardium as the line of communication between the Heart and the Tan Tien and the Triple Warmer as instrumental in the production of post natal Shen. This nourishment of the source chi and production of Shen are necessary for the energetic transformations sought after in Tai Chi Chuan.

Not only does the sinking of the chi to the Tan Tien nourish the source chi but it also activates it. In some Taoist practices and in some approaches to Tai Chi Chuan this activation of the source can reach the point where the chi actually causes a physical vibration in the Tan Tien by its activity. This activated energy is directed throughout the body by the mind in advanced practitioners.

The mind directed chi is useful in combat situations and initiates higher energetic transformations.

The martial literature is filled with advice to root the feet. This rooting does not refer to the mere strengthening of the legs but to the actual transfer of source (root) chi to the soles of the feet, especially the acupoint Kidney 1.

We Know that the Triple Warmer and the Eight Extraordinary Vessels are intimately concerned with bringing source chi to the extremities. With proper training, this rooting can actually extend beneath the feet into the ground. At a higher level of development the rooting not only anchors the practitioner but can be used as a dynamic moving force to uproot the opponent,

In this case the practitioners root energy will move to the opponents root and disturb his balance.

For those practitioners involved in "spirit" work, proper rooting will accelerate their practices and provide an important balancing safety factor.

Often "spirit" techniques aim at developing the energetic ability for various states of consciousness to leave the body through the top of the head. Whatever the purposes or techniques involved, being able to extend consciousness down as well as up will be of great benefit. "Spirit" practices are still in the realm of Yin and Yang and it is of the utmost importance to maintain balance. The ability to go down greatly enhances the ability to go up. It also opens a safety route for those who may get "too far out".

Man is the energetic manifestation between heaven and earth. We access earth through the feet and heaven through the head. Development of either access route without the balanced development of the other is very dangerous.

A great many so called psychics do have some extra-ordinary sensitivities but they can be manifestations of imbalances rather than true development. In the vast amount of literature about peoples psychic experiences we often see that the most powerful experiences came at a time of severe illness, stress, or a near death experience. These are times of great imbalance and do produce extremes of energetic phenomena.

If psychic information is channeled through a medium of extreme imbalance, the information must be suspect, Pure energy channeled through an unbalanced medium is unlikely to be pure.

Systems that propose to teach extra sensitivities that lack energetic balance are dangerous to our health and well being on many levels.

Moving Together

Moving together is truly difficult. Even on the gross physical level this principle involves years and years of attention and refinement. We are all familiar with the descriptions in the classical literature on this subject. It seems fairly simple to comprehend. However, putting the intellectual comprehension into the bodies physical, energetic, and spiritual systems is another story.

I first learned Tai Chi Chuan from my teacher as a series of static postures. His purpose in teaching me this way was to familiarize me with the individual postures and allow me to get a minimal grasp of moving together within the transitions to each new posture.

The difficulty in physically moving together within a single transition is compounded by the necessity of all the various body parts to be at the same degree of completion of their individual movements at the same time.

For example, let us imagine that a given transition from one posture to the next takes one minute. Within this transition each body part will have to move a different distance. The legs may move a distance of four feet, the arms six feet the trunk three feet etc.

All parts of the body must begin their movements at the same time. At the thirty second period in time each individual body part should be half way through its movement-the leg would have moved two feet, the arms three feet.

Add to this coordination of time and distance the difficulty of keeping every movement circular, relaxed, and in harmony with the other movements and the problem becomes almost insurmountable.

The eyes must also be coordinated with the movements of the body. It is said that the eyes control the spirit and in using the eyes correctly the spirit can be trained.

In Tai Chi Chuan, the eyes should at first follow the lead hand—the hand doing the most yang or aggressive work. At a later stage of development the eyes will lead the hands.

When the energy and spirit are even more developed, the ears will at first follow the energy and later lead it.

When the basic postures have been grasped in the static form, they are linked together in one continuous ever changing flow of harmonious movement.

After a certain amount of time and energy is directed towards moving together on the physical level(we are talking years here) the practitioner will become aware of the sensation of energy moving in the body.

Each posture is designed to concentrate the energy predominantly in one arm and one leg. The postures were designed this way both to accelerate the natural flow of energy in the body, and to facilitate the increase of energetic awareness of the practitioner. At a more advanced level the practitioner will be able to control at which part of the body the energy will be concentrated.

Once the state of energetic awareness has been realized, the idea of moving together must entail both moving together physically and conforming your energetic awareness to the physical movements.

With time and proper training the awareness of energy will gradually become control of energy by the mind. At this point the mind will move the energy and the energy will begin to move the body.

Advanced practitioners are able to move the energy within (and outside) their bodies at will without the necessity of physical movement. This is a great boon to training because it enables one to practice in otherwise impossible circumstances such as sitting on an airplane or in a boring class. This method can also be used as a very powerful meditation.

After more years of practice the body mind and energy will move together quite freely. One of the results of this free harmonious movement will be the awakening of the spirit which will also begin to move with the mind/energy/body.

In time, the spirit will become the leader in the movements of our entire beings.

Training the fast Tai Chi Chuan form is one very potent method of training the spirit. By the time one learns the fast form, his body and energy should be moving quite freely together. To allow the spirit to move, it is necessary to have a clear mind. Even with body and energy moving together in the slow form it is possible for the mind to wander.

In the fast form it is more difficult for the mind to wander. The mind will be focused on the task at hand. This focus with the body and energy in harmonious movement forces the spirit to become involved in the activity. With more time and practice this forcing will change to an opening or relaxing of the mind to allow the spirit to control the practice.

One of the manifestations of spirit, energy, and body moving together is the appearance of light within the body. The practitioner will see, with his upper Tan Tien(third eye area between and behind the middle of the eyebrows) light circulating throughout his body. At a more advanced level the light will be seen to penetrate the bones. "You should be able to expand your consciousness to fill your body without any gaps or dark spot."[34]

With a combination of his two regular eyes and the third eye the practitioner will also see the light emanating from his body—his aura. The more light circulating within, the more light will emanate from the body. As time goes on the practitioner will begin to be able to see the light in others also.

Each succeeding stage of training requires a more minutely attentive attitude towards moving together. There are many more advanced and other intermediate stages that were not discussed here. The point is to constantly exercise your imagination in moving together at ever more subtle levels.

We often read of "Listening Energy", that state in which one practitioner will know the energetic intent of another before physical movement takes place. The usual explanation of this energetic phenomena is that through long hours of pushing hands training a sort of super sensitivity can be developed through the sense of touch. I believe this is true, but there is another aspect of listening energy that I have not seen discussed.

The energy used for extraordinary development is stored in and channeled through the Kidneys. In Oriental Medicine, each of the yin organs has an opening through which it relates to the outside world. The opening of the Kidneys is the ear.

When energy moves freely through the body a distinct sound is audible to the practitioner. In more advanced practitioners when the energy enters the bones and circulates at that level a different sound manifests.

I believe that the past masters could move together with their opponents energy and literally hear their opponents energetically manifested sound. Because of the previously discussed relationships of energy to Shen the intent of the opponent would be very clear to one who could move together within him.

At more advanced levels of development the practitioner should be able to hear an opponents energy without the need for physical contact.

Relaxing

Our teachers constantly remind us to relax. Relaxing on the many levels addressed by Tai Chi Chuan is one of the principle focuses of the art.

Relaxing of the physical body entails using only those muscles necessary to keep the body in proper form throughout all movements. If there is tension in any muscle not required for the performance of the form your energy flow will be impeded. With time and attention to practice the muscles will gradually begin to "soften" and allow smooth fluid movements with minimal energy expended by the muscles. The muscle energy utilized in the form will become less and less as the physical body begins to be supported by your developing life force or chi.

The "softer" you become, the more chi or life force your system will be able to transport and transform. We already know that the Triple Warmer can function to bring the chi of air to the Tan Tien. We also know that the Triple Burner is associated with the connective tissue of the body.

As the connective tissue relaxes, more chi can reach the Tan Tien and as more chi reaches the Tan Tien more energy will be transformed and transported in the body.

The mind must also relax in Tai Chi Chuan. Throughout your training career, different levels of attention will be required of your mind. As you progress, the new levels of attention will always be of a more subtle nature.

For example, on day one your mind will be fully occupied in just holding a physical posture. By day three thousand your mind will be involved in holding energetic sensation if not in even more esoteric phenomena.

The path from one form of attention to a new and more subtle form involves relaxing the mind enough to let go of the coarser level and immerse in the more subtle level.

As one becomes more advanced the mind must relax beyond attention. One of the often quoted classics makes reference to the fact that if there is chi there is no power. Because we think of chi as power this seems strange. The answer lies in looking at different levels of power in the body.

With chi supporting the body we do increase our power dramatically. When one has progressed to the point of the chi moving smoothly in the body with the mind we say the chi follows the mind or where there is mind there is chi. This is an admirable stage of development but not yet in the realm of spirit.

To reach even higher development and function in the world of spirit the mind must be totally relaxed—thus no mind and no chi. "If we speak of "transforming the chi into spirit," then we must go further and discuss how "the consciousness should be on the spirit and not on the chi. If it is on the chi there will be blocks."[35]

From a trained observers eye there will be a great deal of chi present in the practitioner but as the practitioners body, mind, chi, and spirit will be one he will perceive no chi. This is true relaxation and high Tai Chi Chuan.

Theme Training

Through the years of training different aspects of the art will have to be emphasized in the form at different times. One of the most valuable approaches to emphasizing one aspect of Tai Chi Chuan through the form is theme training.

Theme training concentrates your attention on a particular theme you have chosen for that training period.

For instance, you may choose to accent depth of stance one day. In this case you would do the entire form but sink the physical body as low as correctly possible throughout the form. This will of course necessitate moving a little more quickly than your average speed because your legs will be rather uncomfortable.

At a more advanced stage on this sinking idea you could accent the depth of your energetic root rather than just the depth of the physical stance. In this case you would sink your root beneath your feet into the ground. You would then feel all the changes of the set energetically take place beneath your feet.

Your imagination can produce many themes to work on such as accenting the right or left arm or leg, relaxing the shoulders, keeping the spine straight, focusing energy at specific acupuncture points during the form, directing the energy with the eyes or the ears, directing the energy with the third eye or from outside the body via the top of the head, going as slow as possible, etc. etc.

Whatever theme you choose, this method of training will not only allow you but actually force you to study, feel, and increase your awareness of one area of your form and how it relates to other areas. This can lead to profound and very inspirational realizations about many aspects of Tai Chi Chuan.

Theme training should be used with discretion and in proper balance with your overall training program.

Time and Timing

Timing in the Tai Chi Chuan form is explained in the section on Moving Together. It basically involves the controlled movement of the body that produces the effect of all body parts moving harmoniously together. Each physical body part, during its arc of movement, should begin its intended path at the same time, reach the middle at the same time, and ends at the same time.

As one progresses to energetic and spirit training, the subtle mind spirit, energy aspects of training become more important than the physical movements but even at this level coordinated training produces faster results.

Two other areas where time concerns most of us are the time it takes to do the form and the time it takes to become proficient in Tai Chi Chuan.

There are several theorys on how long a form should take.

In recent years several versions of a short form have been gaining acceptance. Some teachers feel that people won't take the time to do the traditional long forms but will do a shortened version. They feel doing a short version is better than doing nothing at all. One man in San Francisco advertises on his brochure that three to five minutes a day is enough to help your health. Sounds GREAT to me.

Some reputable proponents of shorter forms feel that repetition is one of the most important factors in developing natural responses, so present short forms that can be repeated many times during a training session.

The average length of time recommended for completing the traditional forms seems to be from twenty to thirty minutes. If you add to this time one hour of stance work, one hour of chi gung, and one hour of meditation each day you will have a pretty fair training program.

My own teacher believes forms should be done very slowly. He encourages me to spend from one to two hours on each form. I have never personally done a form for more than an hour but I believe a two hour continuous session would be very inspirational.

Time spent in the form depends on several things. If your mind is disturbed on a particular day your form will probably be done faster. If you are working your stances or your legs are sore from the the hour form you did the day before it will also go faster.

If your mind is clear, legs are not sore and you are not maxing out the depth of your stance you will be able to move much more slowly.

The bottom line here is that you must regulate the speed of your form to your physical and mental condition and to your training goals.

The length of time it takes to become proficient in this limitless art depends on your view of proficiency. Most practitioners, if they plan to train with peace of mind, must accept the fact that training every day to the best of their ability is proficiency. Because of the inherent nature of correct training—awareness always increases faster than ability— finding satisfying progress is difficult.

I was recently told by a friend that in a magazine question and answer article a famous master from China said that if you train eight hours a day for ten years you might be able to do the form fairly well. However this amount of training would still not produce a high level of the art.

I feel that this is a fairly accurate evaluation of the time and effort necessary for attaining mediocre proficiency in Tai Chi Chuan.

What satisfies the goals of one practitioner may not be the correct way for another.

To some practitioners just memorizing the form and being able to do it once or twice a week would be considered proficient

To others, proficiency may not be acknowledged until they were beyond acknowledgements.

Each person has his own goals and his own way. The art of Tai Chi Chuan is broad enough to accommodate many diverse approaches and involvements.

Nature Observation and Stalking

Most authorities believe that the Taoists developed their philosophy through the observation of natural phenomena. The basic concepts of both the I Ching and the Theory of the Five Elements were derived from observation of natural cycles and changes.

The sages who formulated these theories lived much closer to nature than we do today. We often read in the legend/histories of Taoism and Tai Chi Chuan of sages that lived in the mountains and developed various techniques for energetic development. Many of the techniques, such as Chi Gung and Tai Chi Chuan were passed on but little is mentioned of the skills and practices involved in living the life of a mountain sage.

The esoteric practices have been divorced from the environment from which they originated.

My purpose is not to suggest that it is necessary to be a recluse/survivalist to learn Tai Chi Chuan. This is certainly not the case.

However, learning more about nature and immersing oneself in the energy patterns of the wilderness can be helpful for your understanding and development in Tai Chi Chuan.

According to Tom Brown, one of the greatest "Nature Teachers" of this time, just spending time in wilderness areas changes your brains' energy patterns as measured by biofeedback equipment.

These changes reflect a more relaxed state of mind, a mind more receptive to the wisdom and flow of the natural environment.

This state of receptivity is one of the goals of training Tai Chi Chuan.

Many of the requirements for nature observation, stalking, and Tai Chi Chuan are the same.

A clear mind is necessary in Tai Chi Chuan to observe the energetic qualities of your training, focus your attention on the task at hand, and eventually escape the realm of the intellect.

In nature observation and stalking, a clear mind is needed to observe the energetic quality of your surroundings, to focus your attention on the area of interest or animal being stalked, and to immerse yourself in the flow of the wilderness.

This immersing is particularly important in stalking. Animals seem to be able to sense mind chatter and clearing the mind makes stalking much more fruitful.

One of Tai Chi Chuan's' practice strategies is slow, smooth, rounded movement. This allows precise physical control and detailed energetic observation/awareness within.

This same movement strategy is necessary in nature observation and stalking.

Moving slowly, smoothly, and roundly in the wilderness gives one the chance to see more of the environment, and to scare fewer animals away. Animals have poor color perception but very acute shape and movement perception.

In stalking, one must move slowly as in the practice of Tai Chi Chuan. The movements must be smooth and rounded as animals will notice a square or jerky movement much more readily than a soft, rounded, slow movement.

These movement requirements approximate those of Tai Chi Chuan. In stalking, the awareness must extend to the external environment. One must be careful not to brush against bushes, step on dry leaves or twigs, or disturb other animals that may be in the same area as the one being stalked.

If the animal being stalked happens to look in your direction all movement must stop. This means you can be forced to hold some very awkward positions for considerable lengths of time. Holding these positions is excellent stance work and aids in developing balance and the ability to always be in balance while moving.

Time can be a problem in Tai Chi Chuan, nature observation, and stalking.

Often our minds delegate a set amount of time for certain activities and put so much focus on the time allowed that we fail to take full advantage of our opportunities.

Although it is unpractical to totally ignore time, it is important to be as fully absorbed in your present endeavor as possible.

"Know the soul before you know the name and you will experience much more."[36]

This advice was given to readers of Tom Brown Field Guide to Nature Observation and Tracking to encourage them to get beyond the intellectual analyzation and naming of things and to become more involved in direct experience.

Similar advice was given to me by my teacher. One day I asked him if it was important to learn the names of the individual postures of Tai Chi Chuan. His answer was that a thousand people could know the names but only one or two could do the posture correctly.

I do feel that it is both interesting and historically respectful to learn the names of the postures. but direct experience is the only way to know the postures themselves. It is far more respectful to put the time and effort into knowing the posture than to simply know the name.

In nature observation and in Tai Chi Chuan we often overlook the obvious and thereby miss opportunities for advancing our knowledge and awareness.

Every plant and animal is a unique individual, a magical source of infinite information on many levels. The marvels of nature are inexhaustible.

This marvelous inexhaustibility is also embodied in every aspect of Tai Chi Chuan. "The commonplace is only the self-constructed wall that separates us from the marvelous."[37]

Each time we practice a posture of Tai Chi Chuan it is different, inside and out. Everything changes. We are not the same person this afternoon that we were this morning. Our energy is different, internal and external environment different, emotions different, etc.

Be aware of the differences. Use that awareness to increase your expertise and open yourself to the marvels of being.

Prejudices hamper our experience of nature and our development in Tai Chi Chuan.

Many of the most rewarding observations of nature occur when we have given up our prejudices about being wet, cold, dirty, etc. and have allowed ourselves the freedom to be part of aspects of nature we usually avoid.

Likewise, in Tai Chi Chuan, we have to get beyond our intellectual conceptions of what we expect development to be, how we expect things to feel, and how we expect to progress. We must open ourselves to the direct experience of training and let that ever changing experience show us all that is within our capacity to see.

Nature observation and stalking exercise areas of our senses that are often overlooked in studio training. To see and not be seen in the wilderness demands the use of the eyes, ears, nose, skin, and deeper senses and thought processes in ways that are not ordinarily required.

These demands provide us with a valuable opportunity to express ourselves on unusual levels and greatly profit from the experience.

Tai Chi Chuan, Health, and Longevity

From studies of the literature regarding the history of practitioners of Tai Chi Chuan it is obvious that to maximize health and longevity one must practice more than the Tai Chi Form.

From pictures and written material we find records of renowned exponents of Tai Chi Chuan being overweight, lacking stamina, and dying at a relatively early age.

Proper diet, balanced lifestyle and the many other ingredients that produce a natural, harmonious being must be present to receive the full benefit of training Tai Chi Chuan.

The inner balance developed by training should produce a balanced life.Practicing natural harmony in your life should help your energetic development.

It is difficult to cover all the bases in our efforts to maintain harmony in the modern world. The pressures of the workplace, family, friends, and attention to the issues we confront every day suck as pollution, political turmoil, transportation, etc. all require time and energy.

There are some simple precautions we can take to aid ourselves in energetic development. We can make sure that we eat a properly balanced diet. Generally properly balanced means eating a wide variety of foods without over depencence on any one. Avoiding overuse of refined sugars, coffee, alcohol and greasy foods will definitely pay off in better physical health.

Proper diet guidelines are available from many sources. One point my teacher makes is that some red meat in the diet is advisable.

Various herbs can be helpful in maintaining health and well being. As everybodys conditions and needs are different, it is advisable to check with a licensed practitioner of Oriental Medicine to find the proper herbal aids to maintaining your health.

Proper rest is essential for good health. Training three or four hours a day, working, and taking care of the business of life requires a substantial energy output. The body needs sleep to recuperate. As a general rule, younger people need more sleep than older people and those who expend more energy in working and training need more sleep than those who expend less.

Here again everyone is different so there can be no hard and fast rules for the amount of time one should sleep. Most people will find six to eight hours adequate.

Magnets

One of the most valuable assets we have for aiding our health/energetic development is explained more fully in the book, Magnetic Healing and Meditation. The techniques discussed here are all more fully explained in that book.

any intervention in your energetic systems should be attempted only under the direct care of a legally licensed specialist in Oriental Medicine. The techniques presented here are for information and entertainment purposes only.

As an acupuncturist, I have been studying the effects of various body acupuncture techniques on meditation for several years.

The results of these studies were encouraging but it seemed impractical to have these techniques utilized by the energetic development community at large.

With my introduction to Koryo Hand Acupuncture and subsequent work with magnets, I found a medium that gave even more encouraging results and could be utilized by a much greater segment of the population.

The use of magnets in the energetic systems of the body help create balance and can be a definite aid to energetic development.

Several long time martial arts and yoga practitioners in the San Francisco area used magnets in their training for a period of one month and reported substantial benefits (see back cover of Magnetic Healing and Meditation.

Magnets are not a substitute for training. They can be useful in balancing various levels of the energetic system and augmenting many training practices but will not take the place of hard work on the many levels previously mentioned.

With any increase in energetic balance we will have a more certain advancement in the quest for energetic development.

On page 82 of Magnetic Healing and Meditation we see a diagram relating to the Triple Warmer Treatment.

Treating the lower warmer with moxabustion is one of the very best overall constitutional strengtheners I have found. The lower warmer is the location of the Source Chi. This treatment strengthens the basic vitality of the body.

I usually recommend treating the middle warmer also. This strengthens the digestive system which nourishes the source chi also. The energy and substance used to heal any of our imbalances reaches those imbalances after being transformed through the digestive system.

On pages 93-94 we find the Adrenal Treatment. This treatment balances the basic fire and water of the body. The Adrenal Treatment is excellent to augment meditative practices that require a clear mind centered in the Tan Tien. It has the effect, through balancing basic Kidney fire and water, of sinking the mind to the Tan Tien.

The Tokito Treatment on pages one hundred twenty to one hundred twenty four is my favorite. This technique uses the eight extraordinary vessels to access that level of energy in the body that precedes form(Pericardium/ Triple Warmer). This treatment is a very powerful rejuvenator and balancer of the deepest layers of energy we can access with external intervention.

The magnet combination I originally used to study the effects of magnets on Tai Chi Chuan practice is found on page one hundred thirty-five. As participants in this study I used six practitioners who had been involved in training Tai Chi Chuan at least eight years.I asked them to wear this particular arrangement of magnets (after diagnosing them to be sure the combination was appropriate) three or four times a week during their practice. The study lasted for one month.

At the end of the study period, all six practitioners reported noticing an increase in awareness of energetic flow if not an actual increase in the flow during their practice periods.

It is difficult to establish whether the flow of energy increased, the awareness of the flow increased, or both awareness and energy flow increased.

In any case, all participants found the experience helpful and continue to use magnets in their training.

I chose this treatment (page 135) because it activates both Yin and Yang Chiao Mo. These two extraordinary Vessels control the movement of Yin and Yang in the body. The Ren and Du Mo, which are the main vessels used for the Taoist Microcosmic Orbit energy transformations are also activated.

I believe this combination also aligns all seven chakras in their proper rotational balance and activates the upper Tan Tien or Third Eye.

For people doing visualization meditations, this combination is very useful as it circulates a lot of energy through the head and stimulates the Third Eye. I mention these magnet combinations as examples of ways to approach augmenting your Tai Chi Chuan practice. None of these methods should be used without the guidance of a qualified and legally licensed Oriental Medical Practitioner.

There are many other appropriate techniques useful for augmenting development. For instance, sedating the liver for relaxing the tendons and toning the kidneys for strengthening the basic chi and supporting the bones can be extremely useful if appropriate.

With the guidance of a properly qualified practitioner you can get your individual imbalances diagnosed and learn the proper magnet treatments for correcting them.

This will surely speed up your progress towards good health and proficiency in Tai Chi Chuan.

The Tai Chi Chuan Classics

"The T'ai Chi Ch'uan Classics is an attempt to state (selectively, even arbitrarily, and by no means exhaustible) the irrevocable principles of Taoism in terms of martial arts," [38]

The Tai Chi Chuan Classics are a collection of writings by several past masters of the art. They describe various aspects of Tai Chi Chuan and explain the path to energetic development.

Because the art of Tai Chi Chuan is one of direct experience, no words can reveal its "secrets". However, direct experience of the art will reveal the secrets of the words.

Understanding of the Classics follows your own development. The more you develop through training, the more you will understand.

Even though we can not expect complete understanding of the classics we will find in them clear guidelines for each stage of our development.

Many books on Tai Chi Chuan contain interesting and informative translations of some of the classics.

Let us take a brief energetic look at some parts of these translations.

The T'ai Chi Ch'uan Ching by Cheng San-Feng contains a passage translated these two ways by their respected translators.

"The ch'i (breath) should be excited, the shen (spirit) should be internally gathered."[39] In the preface to this book the authors explain that excited was used to connote the idea of a box with all the oceans of the world inside sloshing back and forth. The preface goes on to explain that the ch'i circulates in the body this way.

The same passage is translated by Dr. Yang Jwing- Ming in Advanced Yang Style Tai Chi Chuan as: "Chi should be full and stimulated, Shen (Spirit) should be retained internally."[40]

This translation is explained as meaning the chi from the Tan Tien should fill the body and the mind should be in control.

Energetically, when the shen is internally gathered in the Tan Tien—by attaining an open line of communication between the heart and Kidneys via the Pericardium—and presuming the Tan Tien itself is appropriately developed, the yin/yang aspects of the body will naturally be set in motion.

The practitioner will feel an energetic sensation of internal sloshing back and forth much like a slinky moving from hand to hand.

If the practitioner is sitting in meditation at this time his body may physically respond by gently rocking from side to side. If doing the Tai Chi Chuan form the sloshing will be mediated by the movements of the form.

This gentle rocking motion, inside and out, is reminiscent of a baby being rocked in its mothers' arms. We all know that rocking can relax and calm a baby. Perhaps the external motion reminds the baby of the yin/yang energetic changes experienced naturally in the comfort and safety of the womb.

It has been expressed by many health experts that walking is one of the best exercises for overall well being. By its nature, walking causes a natural yin/yang left/right energy shift in the body.

The construction of the Tai Chi Chuan form aims at and facilitates the natural left/right yin/yang energetic changes within the body.

In meditation, when the Tan Tien begins to develop and become full of chi it will vibrate in most practitioners. This vibration moves back and forth between the back of the body(Ming Men) and the front of the body (Tan Tien) at the level of the lower abdomen.

After sufficient energy has gathered and the Tan Tien is appropriately developed, the Shen will gather within. At this point the energetic sensation of movement will begin to move from side to side in a rocking motion.

From the Tan Tien this rocking or sloshing sensation will spread throughout the body. The body will feel like a container filled with water that is shifting back and forth.

There are actually three centers in the body referred to as Tan Tien. They are the lower Tan Tien—below the navel, the middle Tan Tien—at the solar plexus or mid-chest, and the upper Tan Tien—between and behind the eyebrows.

The signs of energetic transformation including vibrating and rocking, can take place in any of the three centers as they develop.

In many of the translations of the Classics we find expressed the idea of being rooted in the feet.

We have already discussed the idea of the source chi (root) being transported from the Tan Tien to the extremities via the Triple Warmer and the Eight Extraordinary Vessels.

That idea is one very valid energetic explanation of these passage.

Another view is to consider the energetic nourishment obtained through our root (feet).

At certain levels of development it is possible to be nourished directly from the energy of earth (Yin) and Heaven (Yang). We gather this nourishment through our feet and head respectively. The energy from Earth is more directly connected with the physical body and the energy from Heaven is more connected with the spirit.

The references to being suspended by a string from the top of the head could refer to the connection with the Heaven energy.

When we are open to these energetic nourishments from Heaven and Earth, we feel the yin drawn up to the Tan Tien and the yang drawn down to the Tan Tien.

When these two energies meet at the center, they feel like the Tai Chi Symbol looks—a swirling energetic ball of nourishment.

The Classics state that the Yi or I (mind) should control the movements of the body from within. The Chinese character for I is translated as mind, idea, or thought. It is composed of two parts. One part means heart/mind and the other means verbally expressed thoughts.

In Oriental Medicine the I is the visceral entity connected with the Spleen, which controls the muscles and flesh of the body.

The Kidneys control the bones. Chen or Zhi is the visceral entity of the kidneys as is translated as will. The character for Chen or Zhi is also comprised of two parts, one of which means mind/heart and the other means foot. The Kidney channel in Oriental Medicine begins on the bottom of the foot, at the point where yin is most easily absorbed from the earth. Movement in Tai Chi Chuan, according to the classics begins in the foot.

Ancient medical books tell us that the I and Zhi are the controllers of Shen and Jing.

This is the energetic connection for all movements in advanced Tai Chi Chuan where the idea (I-spleen) animated by will (Zhi-Kidneys) leads shen (Heart) and Jing (Kidneys) to manifest through movement of the chi which moves the body.

In speaking of substantial and insubstantial, many translators explain that if one arm or leg or side of the body is full, the opposite member or side will be empty. Of course there are varying degrees of fullness and emptiness. It is extremely important to differentiate full and empty in your practice. The Tai Chi Chuan form itself is designed to facilitate this differentiation.

With more advanced development, the fullness or emptiness is determined by the mind rather than the physical form.

At an even more advanced stage, when the source chi fully circulates in its undifferentiated state, full or empty can manifest anywhere in the body at any time—including simultaneously.

In various translations of the classics we read about the spirit ascending to the top of the head and the chi sticking to the spine and being released by the back.

It is generally known that Du Mo ascends the spine to the top of the head and the Kidneys control the backbone (as well as store energy).

The kidneys store both Jing and Chi which must enter the bones for superior development in Tai Chi Chuan.

Years ago, my teacher mentioned an area in the upper back and explained that it was a little known point but very important as a storage place for power.

I believe that this point was Urinary Bladder 11 which is 1.5 to 2 body inches lateral to the spinous process of the first thoracic vertebrae.

In Oriental Medicine this point is a major influential point for the bones, which energetically links it to the kidneys (storage of energy—control bones).

When the chi flows up Du Mo towards the head, it reaches Urinary Bladder 11 through a connecting channel. Both the Triple Warmer and Small Intestine channels of the arm are also connected to this point.

The physical sensation of the rising chi can be so strong that the practitioner feels as if he were being picked up by the nape of the neck much like a kitten is picked up and carried by its mother.

The energy can be so strong that it will physically cause the spine to bend like a bow—which is also mentioned in the classics.

Activation of this point will cause the chi/jing to enter the bones, greatly increase overall circulation and add support to the rise of the spirit.

Another interesting translation from the classics refers to the origin of all the postures being the waist. This follows our diagram of the energetic structure of the body perfectly, as the waist (source) is the precursor to the five elements and the eight trigrams.

Proper use of the waist is also an essential element in all of the postures.

Within the classical writings there are many instances where a phrase has meaning on more than one level.

While it is interesting to intellectualize about the deeper meanings, understanding on the intellectual level does not equal energetic development.

Because Tai Chi Chuan is such an all encompassing art, it is valuable to study the classics, but to learn them takes direct experience.

Meditation and Chi Gung

For the purposes of this brief discussion we shall define meditation as any technique used to control the mind or energy practiced in a sitting position.

Tai Chi Chuan itself is often called a moving meditation and there are many techniques done in postures other than sitting that are referred to as meditations.

The opinions of experts as to whether meditation is necessary for development in Tai Chi Chuan are varied. This is no cause for surprise as expert opinions on almost every aspect of the art are varied.

Some experts say that Tai Chi Chuan itself is meditation or better than meditation. Other experts say meditation is the yin aspect of the art and the physical form is the yang aspect.

My teacher does encourage meditation , which is part of his system of Chi Gung. He says that meditation, Tai Chi Chuan, and Chi Gung are all the same—once your energetic being is developed enough to allow free circulation of vital energy.

On the other hand he does not believe you can get this development with Tai Chi Chuan alone.

There is little doubt that meditation can be a valuable tool for quieting the mind. A quiet mind is necessary for the correct practice of Tai Chi Chuan.

It may be easier to develop a quiet mind through sitting meditation rather than through practice of the Tai Chi Chuan form. Form practice, especially in the early decades, does require some thought.

In later, more advanced stages, it may be possible to practice the form with a clear mind. Meditations of various sorts can be used not only to quiet the mind, but also to help speed up the development of energetic centers, pathways, and transformations in the body.

This in turn will help the overall development of Tai Chi Chuan.

Chi Gung

Chi Gung, or breathing exercises, can be another valuable aspect of Tai Chi Chuan training.

Here again some authorities say Tai Chi Chuan is Chi Gung and others believe that Chi Gung Techniques other than the Tai Chi Chuan form should be practiced.

Generally the three requirements for preforming Chi Gung are control of the breath, the body, and the mind.

Training the Tai Chi Chuan form can easily fit these requirements.

Many teachers feel that the Chi Gung aspect to Tai Chi Chuan is the co-ordination of the breath with the movements of the form.

This co-ordination usually involves inhaling on movements that go up or toward the body and exhaling on movements that go down or away from the body.

Other authorities suggest natural breathing is the appropriate way to train the form.

Many of the teachers who support the co-ordination of breath and form theory say that eventually one must forget the breath and respond naturally.

My teacher believes that the form should be practiced with natural breathing—but that breathing exercises are absolutely necessary outside of the form.

Coordinating the breath with the form has two drawbacks.

First, it limits the speed of the form to faster than some people want to go. With practice one can develop a great deal of respiratory control, but the co-ordination of breath with movement can still be limiting.

Second, the form does not always expand and contract or move up and down in perfectly alternating cycles. In other words, one posture may move towards the body (inhale) and the next posture may move up (inhale).

This can be very hard on respiration or force the practitioner to move through the two postures faster than he wishes.

The remedy for these two conditions is to coordinate the breath with the extremes of the physical expansion or contraction and upward or downward motion. This means you can take a little cheating breath in between those postures that do not alternate conveniently.

Both theories have been used by noteworthy practitioners.

Eighteen Buddha Hands

The Eighteen Buddha Hands is a set of breathing that was originally taught in China by Ta-Mo, a highly developed Buddhist Master from India.

When Ta-Mo came to China he settled at the Shaolin Monastery. Finding the monks at the Monastery frail and weak, he taught them a system of breathing exercises to aid them in their physical health and their spiritual accomplishment. The Eighteen Buddha Hands were part of that system.

Later they were adopted by several systems of Kung Fu to help develop internal power.

In practicing this system, the breath is coordinated with the movements of the body almost exactly as recommended by some Tai Chi Chuan experts.

However, the key to inhaling and exhaling lies not in the direction of arm and body movements during the exercises, but in the action of the rib cage and chest.

If the chest and rib cage expand, the movement calls for an inhalation. If the chest and rib cage contract the movement calls for an exhalation. this pattern fits the usual pattern for Tai Chi Chuan quite closely.

In most cases as the hands and body rise the chest expands and we inhale. As the hands and body sink the chest compresses and we exhale.

Likewise, as the arms move toward the body the chest expands and we inhale and as the hands move away from the body the chest compresses and we exhale.

There are a few instances (chapter two for example) where the hands move away from the body—toward the sides—and the chest expands so you inhale. As the hands move back toward the body—from the sides—your chest compresses so you exhale.

I am including the Eighteen Buddha Hands Internal System here because it is a simple, valuable exercise that can be used to augment any martial arts practice. It is especially good for those who want to practice Chi Gung but have no system of their own.

Befor practicing any exercise you should consult a Physician M.D. Carefully explain your intention, have a complete physical examination, and receive your M.D.s' approval before you begin.

The exercises presented here are for entertainment and educational purposes only. Any use or misuse of these exercises is the sole responsibility of the reader and the author and Publishers of this book will accept no responsibility for any such use.

In performing the Eighteen Buddha Hands Internal System, the movements should be done as slowly and softly as possible while coordinating the breath to the movements.

The breath should be coordinated with the hand and body movements with each inhale or exhale beginning at the same time as its corresponding body movement and ending at the same time as the body movement stops.

The eyes should follow the hands, except where instructed otherwise.

The mind should be focused on the movement of the hands and the breath.

Each of the Eighteen Chapters in this system has one or more moving exercises followed by a standing exercise.

The standing exercises can be held as long as possible, thus being used as standing meditative or stance work exercises.

Since the entire system may take from forty-five minutes to an hour to perform, I find holding each standing position for eight full breaths is sufficient.

Eight full breaths is the breathing pattern used throughout the system.

Many of the exercises are performed on both the left and right sides. This is accomplished by either doing eight repetitions on the right side followed by eight repetitions on the left side or alternating the exercise in a right left-right-etc. pattern.

If the exercise is to be done as eight repetitions on one side and then eight repetitions on the other side, I will pictorially show only one side. The other side will be the exact opposite.

If the exercise is done in a right-left-right-etc pattern, I will show a picture of each side.

Chapter One
Exercise One

Stand with feet together, arms at the sides looking forward.

Slowly form the hands into fists with palms facing up and raise both fists up along the sides of the body as high as comfortably possible inhaling as in Figure One A

One A

Extend both fists away from the body to arms length, gradually turning the palms downward as they extend, exhaling throughout the movement as in Figure One B.

One B

As the fists reach full extension at shoulder level, open the hands with palms pointed directly forward. Rotate the open palms laterally (towards the sides) until the fingers point downward. When the fingers point downward, form fists with the hands and return the fists to the sides of the body—inhaling. The revolving palm just mentioned is used in several other exercises in this series. Whenever it is used it is a transition motion between two other movements. While performing this revolving hand manipulation the first half of the movement is done while still exhaling and the second half is done while beginning to inhale.

Perform this extension-exhale-revolve palms- retraction inhale movement of the arms eight repetitions.

At the end of the eighth repetition, you should be in the position of figure one A with your lungs full of air.

Exhale.

Exercise two

Raise both hands overhead with the fists gradually turning so the palms face forward—inhaling as in Figure One C.

One C

Page 94

Bend at the waist and extend the fists downward to touch the ground in front of the toes -exhaling as in Figure one D

When reaching the ground with the fists perform the revolving hands again, beginning to inhale half way through the movement.

Now raise the fists, with palms facing your body, and begin to straighten the waist. As the waist straightens and your fists approach the halfway

One D

point on their journey back to the overhead position, gradually turn the fists so they face front again inhaling as in Figure one C.

Repeat this sequence from figure one C to one D-revolve handstand back to figure one C eight times exhaling on the way down and inhaling on the way up.

At the end of the eighth repetition you should be in the position shown in figure one C with your lungs full of air.

Exhale.

Standing

From figure one D open your fists and point your your figures with palms flat and fingers facing upwards towards each other. Look straight upwards and breathe naturally as in figure one E

When finished, stand naturally and wait until your breath returns to normal before going on to the Second Chapter.

One E

Chapter Two
Exercise One

Spread the feet apart with toes pointing out and knees bent as in figure two A. Gently join the palms in front of the chest.

Spread both palms outward towards the sides of the body inhaling as in Figure two B

When the palms reach full extension to the sides, return them to the position in figure two A exhaling.

Repeat this spreading-retracting of the palms eight times.

At the end of the eighth repetition you will be in position two A with the lungs empty.

Exercise Two

Form fists with the hands, raise the forearms to a position parallel to the ground, and stand upright inhaling as in figure two C.

Two A

Two B

Two C

Bend the knees and extend the fists downward with palms facing the body exhaling as in figure Two D.

At the full downward extension, perform the revolving hands manipulation as previously described with palms facing the ground and return to the position Figure Two C inhaling.

Repeat this upward/inhaling downward/exhaling movement eight times.

Two D

At the end of the eighth repetition, you will be in the position shown in Figure Two D with your lungs empty.

Standing

While breathing normally, raise your open palms upward with the fingers pointing toward your sides as in Figure Two E. Look upwards at the space between the palms.

Hold this position for eight breaths.

Two E

Chapter Three

Exercise One

Stand with feet together fists at sides with palms facing upwards, and looking towards the right over the right shoulder inhaling as in Figure Three A.

With the right leg, take a long step to the right while extending both palms to the right side exhaling as in figure Three B. The head should now turn

Three A

so that you are looking over your left shoulder with the left leg straight and the right leg bent.

From this position perform the revolving hands as previously described and return to the position shown in Figure Three A inhaling.

Repeat this step out/exhale step in/inhale sequence eight times.

Next, perform the same eight repetitions on the opposite side—stand looking to left—step with left leg to left side exhaling while pushing palms to the left and looking over the right shoulder— revolve hands and return to standing inhaling.

At the end of the last exercise you will be standing upright with fists at the sides looking over the left shoulder and your lungs will be full of air.

Exhale and breathe normally

Three B

Three C

Exercise Two

Bend the knees with toes apart and raise the left fist above the head and extend the right fist down straight.as in Figure Three C

Now change the arm positions, raising the left arm overhead and lowering the right arm downward.

Repeat this raising and lowering of the arms until each arm has been raised and lowered eight times breathing normally.

Exercise Three

Assume the position pictured in Figure Three D.

Three D

The right arm will be extended above the head, left leg extended resting on the heel, and right leg bent and supporting 90% of the body weight. Inhale as you assume this position.

The right fist will be held at the left side with the palm facing upward.

Bend forward exhaling as in Figure Three E and touch the right fist to the left toe.

Return to the position shown in Figure Three D inhaling.

Three E

Repeat this down and up bending eight times always exhaling on the way down and inhaling on the way up.

Repeat the sequence shown in Figures Three D and E on the opposite side eight times. Now the left arm will be raised, weight on the left leg, right leg extended, etc.

Standing

From the last position exhale and assume a bow and arrow stance. This is pictured in Figure Three F. The rear leg will be straight with the rear hand positioned across the front of the body palm open and pointed towards the opposite side. The front leg will be bent with the front palm raised to the level of the head and

Three F

palm facing upward. Hold this position on both sides for eight breaths. This means there will be two standing exercises after this chapter.

Chapter Four
Exercise One

Place the left foot behind and on the right side of the right foot and hold both fists at the left side with palms facing upwards inhaling as in Figure Four A.

Four A

Extend both arms towards the right with the fists becoming palms exhaling as in Figure Four B.

As the arms reach full extension, with palms facing the right side, perform the revolving hands technique with power and retract the arms to the position of Figure Four A, inhaling.

Repeat this extend/exhale and retract/inhale motion eight times.

Four B

When finished with the eighth repetition change the hand and feet positions to the opposite side and repeat the exercise to the left for eight repetitions.

Exercise Two

Cross the left leg over the right as in Figure Four C. The left leg should support 90% of the body weight with the right toe just touching the ground.

Four C

Roll the left shoulder forward and then the right shoulder forward. Continue this rolling until both shoulders have completed eight revolutions.

Breathing naturally, roll the left shoulder backward and then the right shoulder backward continuing until each shoulder has revolved eight times.

When you have completed the eighth revolution in the backward direction change the footwork pattern to the other side and complete eight forward and eight backward shoulder revolutions again. Breath naturally throughout these revolutions.

Standing

Stand as in Figure Four D with palms extended outward from the front of the body at shoulder level. Hold this posture for eight complete breaths.

Four D

Chapter Five
Exercise One

Move the left foot behind and beside the right foot and rest the left foot on its heel beside the right heel. Place the left arm, with the hand held in a fist palm to the rear, behind the back parallel to the ground. Raise the right arm straight up from the shoulder with the palm facing upward inhaling as in Figure Five A

While closing the palm to form a loose fist, bend forward to touch the right hand to the ground exhaling.as in Figure Five B.

Five A

Straighten the body to the upright
position while placing the right
forearm with half closed fist behind
the back parallels to the ground and
raising the left arm straight up from
the shoulder with palm pointed
upwards fingers pointed towards the
head—inhaling.

Return the left forearm to the
parallel position behind the back and
raise the right hand as in Figure Five
A.

Five B

Repeat the Five A to Five B sequence for eight repetitions.

At the end of the eighth inhale, you will be standing with the
left arm raised and the right arm behind your back. At this time
reverse your feet, placing the right foot behind and to the left
side of the left foot and resting on the right heel.

Do eight repetitions on the left side, bending at the waist and
extending the left hand to the floor exhaling and standing while
extending the right hand overhead inhaling.

Standing

At the end of the eighth repetition on
the left side stand with feet together
hands at the sides with the palms
parallel to the ground as in Figure
Five C. Hold this position at least
eight breaths.

Five C

Chapter Six
Exercise One

Stand with feet together hands at sides. Raise the hands to the waist forming two fists with the palms facing upwards inhaling as in Figure Six A.

Turn the right foot towards the right side and step to the right with the left foot into the bow and arrow stance while extending both hands forward with the palms facing outward exhaling as in Figure Six B.

Perform the revolving hands technique and step back with the left foot to your previous position while retracting your hands in fists inhaling as in Figure Six A

Repeat this sequence eight times exhaling on the step to the right and inhaling on the return step.

Perform the sequence to the opposite side, turning the left foot to the left and stepping to the left with the right foot, pushing the palms outward while exhaling and inhaling as you return to the fists at waist standing position.

Again perform eight repetitions.

Standing

Stand with feet together hands at sides with the palms parallel to the ground as in Figure Six C. Hold this position for at least eight breaths.

Six A

Six B

Six C

Chapter Seven
Exercise One

Stand with knees bent feet spread apart and palms gently touching as in Figure Seven A.

Slowly spread the palms to the sides inhaling as in Figure Seven B.

Raise both palms overhead to gently touch exhaling as in Figure Seven C.

Drop both palms to the previous position inhaling as in Figure Seven D.

Seven A

Seven B

Seven D

Seven C

Bring both palms together in front of the body exhaling as in Figure Seven E.

Standing

Stand with feet together hands at the sides with the palms parallel to the ground as in Figure Seven F. Hold this position for at least eight breaths.

Chapter Eight

Exercise One

Extend right foot to right side of the body resting on the heel with 90% of the body weight on the left foot. Place both hands in fists with palms facing upwards at the waist inhaling.

Extend right fist to the toe of the right foot with the palm facing downward exhaling as in Figure Eight A.

Return right fist to waist and change stance so that left foot is extended and 90% of the body weight is on the right foot—inhaling.

Extend left fist to the left toe exhaling opposite of Figure Eight A.

Repeat this right/left sequence eight times.

Seven E

Seven F

Eight A

Exercise Two

Bring the heels of both feet together and spread the toes. Hold the palms in front of the chest exhaling as in Figure Eight B.

Spread both palms to the sides of the body inhaling as in figure Eight C.

Return palms to the previous position exhaling.

Repeat this spread palms/inhale retract palms/exhale sequence eight times.

Standing

Bend knees, spread the feet apart and grasp the inner thighs opposite of the knees with the hands as in Figure Eight D.

Hold this position for at least eight breaths.

Eight B

Eight C

Eight D

Chapter Nine
Exercise One

Place the left foot behind and on the right side of the right foot resting on its heel and hook the left toe tightly to the right leg.

Bend the right elbow and bring the right fist with the palm facing upwards to a position approximately parallel to the ground with vigor. Slap the right forearm with the left palm to stop the ascent of the right fist. Inhale during this process. The two limbs should meet with firm force as in Figure Nine A.

Nine A

Bend forward extending the right fist to the ground exhaling. Twist the right fist as you extend so that the palm faces your body at full extension. Maintain contact with the left hand as in Figure Nine B.

Return to standing and repeat this exercise for eight repetitions.

Reverse this process and do eight repetitions on the opposite side.

Nine B

Standing

Stand on both heels and look into the palms as in Figure Nine C. Hold this position for eight breaths.

Nine C

Chapter Ten
Exercise One

Stand with feet together hands raised to the sides in fists with palms facing upwards inhaling as in Figure Ten A.

Ten A

Step to the right with the right leg forming a bow stance. As you step extend the left palm to shoulder level in front of the body, hold the right palm across the body pointing to the left side and exhale as in Figure Ten B.

Twist the body to the left making a wide circle with the left hand from the extended forward position to raised above the left shoulder inhaling as in Figure Ten C.

Return to Position Ten A by retracting your right foot while inhaling. Do eight repetitions of this sequence.

Ten B

Repeat the same sequence of stand, step and extend palm, twist back, and return to standing on the left side for eight repetitions.

Ten C

Exercise Two

Spread the legs, bend the knees and sink into a "horse" stance inhaling as in Figure Ten D inhaling.

Push both palms to the right side with vigor exhaling. Retract the hands inhaling and push both palms to the left side exhaling, again with vigor as in Figures Ten D and E.

Repeat this left/right sequence eight times.

Ten D

Standing

Stand with feet together hands at the sides with the palms parallel to the ground as in Figure Ten F. Hold this position for at least eight breaths.

Ten E

Ten F

Chapter Eleven
Exercise One

From a standing position extend the right palm outward and across the front of the body with vigor. At the same time extend the left leg and the left palm outward and across the body exhaling. the left palm should contact the right wrist area to stop the right palm with force as in Figure Eleven A.

Eleven A

Return to standing inhaling.

Repeat the sequence on the left side as in Figure Eleven B

Do eight repetitions of this right/left sequence.

Exercise Two

Extend the right leg out to the right side of the body resting on its heel. Place the right arm with the palm in a fist facing downward across the abdomen inhaling as in Figure Eleven C. Right fist should face down in Figure Eleven C.

Eleven B

Eleven C

Turn to the other side exhaling and as you reach the opposite position with the left leg extended and the right arm up inhale as in Figure Eleven D.

Perform this right/left sequence eight times.

Standing

Stand with feet together hands at the sides with the palms parallel to the ground as in Figure Eleven E

Hold this position for at least eight breathes

Chapter Twelve
Exercise one

Lift the left knee high and spread the hands to the sides as shown in Figure Twelve A inhaling.

Drop the left foot behind and to the right of the right foot as you raise the left palm to touch the left shoulder and forcefully strike the left elbow with the right palm as in Figure Twelve B exhaling.

Return to the position in Figure Twelve A inhaling and repeat the sequence for eight repetitions.

Repeat the same sequence on the right side for eight repetitions.

Eleven D

Eleven E

Twelve A

Exercise two

Stand with the right elbow touching the waist and the left palm facing the right forearm at waist level as in Figure Twelve C inhaling.

Lean forward raising the right palm, bending the right leg pushing the left palm across the abdomen and exhaling as in Figure Twelve D.

Return to Position Twelve C and repeat the sequence for eight repetitions.

Do eight repetitions on the left side also.

Standing

Stand with feet together hands at the sides with palms parallel to the ground as in Figure Twelve E. Hold this position for at least eight breaths.

Twelve B

Twelve C

Twelve E

Twelve D

Chapter Thirteen
Exercise One

Stand with feet together hands at shoulder height as in Figure Thirteen A inhaling.

Bend forward at the waist and extend the palms to the floor with a 180 degree twist as in Figure Thirteen B, exhaling.

Return to the position pictured in Thirteen A inhaling and repeat the sequence for eight repetitions.

Thirteen A

Exercise two

Assume the traditional push-up position with palms on the floor arms extended and toes touching the floor as in Figure Thirteen C inhaling.

Lower your body close to the floor without touching the floor exhaling as in Figure Thirteen D.

Repeat this exercise for eight repetitions.

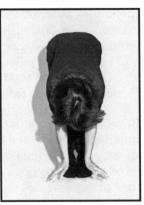

Thirteen B

Thirteen D

Thirteen C

Standing

Stand with heels together toes as far apart as possible (ideally in a straight toes heel heel toe line). Bring the open palms up to point at the sides of the head as in Figure Thirteen E. Hold this position for at least eight breaths.

Chapter Fourteen
Exercise one

From the standing position stretch the left leg straight back, lean towards the front, raise the right hand to slightly higher than the head and push the left palm across the abdomen towards the right side as in Figure Fourteen A exhaling.

Return to the standing position inhaling and raise the left hand to slightly overhead, push the right hand across the abdomen towards the left side, stretch the right leg backwards and lean slightly forward as in Figure Fourteen B exhaling.

Perform this right/left sequence eight times.

Thirteen E

Fourteen A

Fourteen B

Exercise Two

Stretch the right leg far out to the right side, bend the left knee, raise the left hand over the head, and cross the right fist, palm down, to the left side of the waist as in Figure Fourteen C inhaling.

Now switch the entire posture to the opposite side as in Figure Fourteen D. Exhale while switching and inhale as the hand raises above the head.

Fourteen C

Perform this right/left sequence eight times.

Exercise Three

Stand with heels together toes apart (V-shaped), raise the open palms straight overhead with the fingertips pointing to the sides as in Figure Fourteen E inhaling.

Lower the open palms to chest level with palms facing downward exhaling as in Figure Fourteen F.

Fourteen D

Forteen F

Fourteen E

Repeat this raising/inhaling, lowering/exhaling sequence a total of eight times.

Standing

Stand with feet together, hands at sides with the palms facing downward as in Figure Fourteen G. Hold this position for at least eight breaths.

Fourteen G

Chapter Fifteen
Exercise One

Move the right foot behind and to the left side of the left foot and rest it on its heel. Place the left fist with the palm facing upwards at the left side at waist level and place the right forearm across the abdomen with the palm facing the left fist as in Figure Fifteen A inhaling

Fifteen A

Step to the right in a bow and arrow stance while extending the left first outward at shoulder level with the palm facing downwards and the right palm following the movement as in Figure Fifteen B exhaling.

Return to the position shown in Figure Fifteen A and perform eight repetitions of this sequence.

Perform eight repetitions of this sequence on the opposite side.

Fifteen B

Exercise Two

Place the right foot behind and to the left of the left foot. Hold both fists, palm upwards, at the right side of the body waist high as in Figure Fifteen C inhaling.

Step to the right with the right foot forming a bow and arrow stance and extend both fists outward at shoulder height as in Figure Fifteen D exhaling.

Return to the position shown in Figure Fifteen C and perform eight repetitions of this sequence.

Do eight repetitions on the opposite side.

Standing

Stand with feet together hands at the sides with palms facing down parallel to the ground. Hold this position for at least eight breaths.

Chapter Sixteen

Exercise one

Assume the "crab" position as shown in Figure Sixteen A inhaling.

Lower the body to the ground exhaling as in Figure Sixteen B. Perform eight repetitions of this sequence.

Fifteen C

Fifteen D

Sixteen A

Exercise Two

Move the left foot behind and to the right side of the right foot touching the ground with the left heel and hooking the left toes onto the right foot. Raise the right fist to the right shoulder and slap under the right elbow with the left hand with force as in Figure Sixteen C inhaling.

Return to standing and exhale.

Move the right foot behind and to the left side of the left foot, touching the ground with the right heel and hooking the right toes onto the left foot. Raise the left fist to the left shoulder and slap under the left elbow with the right palm with force as in Figure Sixteen D inhaling (feet are incorrect in Figure Sixteen D).

Perform this right/left sequence eight repetitions.

Sixteen B

Sixteen C

Sixteen D

Standing

Stand with feet together hands at the sides with palms facing down parallel to the ground as in Figure Sixteen E. Hold this position for at least eight breaths.

Chapter Seventeen
Exercise one

Lift the right knee high and hold both palms in front of the body facing downwards as in Figure Seventeen A inhaling.

Lower the right foot to the ground and raise the left foot bending it to the rear and leaning slightly forward at the waist with the hands forming fists held at the sides of the body as in Figure Seventeen B exhaling.

Return to the position shown in Figure Seventeen A and perform eight repetitions of this sequence.

Repeat this exercise on the left side for eight repetitions.

Sixteen E

Seventeen A

Seventeen B

Exercise Two

Move the right foot to the right side to form a bow and arrow stance while extending both palms outward at shoulder height as if Figure Seventeen C exhaling.

Turn to the left side inhaling and extend both palms towards the left side at shoulder height exhaling as shown in Figure Seventeen D.

Perform this right/left sequence eight times.

Seventeen C

Standing

Bend both knees and point the toes outward. Hold both fists, palm down at chest level as in Figure seventeen E. Hold this position at least eight breaths.

Seventeen D

Seventeen E

Chapter Eighteen
Exercise one

Sit on the floor with legs outstretched
and hands held above the head as in
Figure Eighteen A inhaling.

Bend at the waist and grasp the outer
sides of both feet as in Figure
Eighteen B exhaling.

Return to the position shown in
Figure Eighteen A inhaling and
perform eight repetitions of this
sequence.

Eighteen A

Standing

Bend the knees and spread the legs
and toes apart as in Figure Eighteen
C. Hold hands straight above the
shoulders and point the fingers
towards the sides of the body as you
breath naturally for at least eight
breaths.

Eighteen B

This concludes our version of the
Eighteen Buddha Hands. Remember
to do the exercises slowly, softly, and
coordinate the body movements and
breath. The standing exercises can be
held as long as possible but holding
them for eight full breaths is both
sufficient and time expedient.

Eighteen C

In concluding this work, let me say that most of the ideas expressed herein are my own interpretations drawn from various sources of information. There may be other interpretations that are equally valid or even more valid. My wish is that this book will serve to add both enjoyment and thought to the readers practice.

T'ai Chi Chuan is a wondrous vehicle through which many different people can realize there individual goals. In this endeavor, I wish you good fortune and good training.

Bibliography

Fundamentals of Tai Chi Chuan Wen by Shan Huang
South Sky Book Company Second Edition 1974

Cheng Man-Ch'ings Advanced Tai—Chi Form Instructions
Compiled and Translated by Douglas Wile
Sweet Ch'i Press 1985

Wu Style Tai Ji Quan by Wang Peisheng & Zeng Weiqi
Hai Feng Publishing Co & Zhaohua Publishing House 1983

Tai chi Ch'uan For Health and Self-Defense by Master T.T.
Liang
Random House, Inc Vintage Books Edition 1977

The Wu Style of Tai Chi Chuan by Tinn Chan Lee
Unique Publications, Inc. 1982

T'ai-Chi Touchstones: Yang Family Secrete Transmissions
Compiled and Translated by Douglas Wile
Sweet Ch'i Press 1983

Master Chengs" Thirteen Chapters on T'ai Chi Ch'uan by Cheng
Man-Ch'ing Translated by Douglas Wile Sweet Ch'i Press 1982

T'ai Chi Ch'uan Ta Wen by Chen Wei-Ming
Translated by Benjamin Pang Jeng Lo and Robert Smith
North Atlantic Books   1985

Yang Style Tai Chi Chuan by Yang Jwing Ming
Unique Publications, Inc. 1982

Advanced Yang Style Tai Chi Chuan Volume One by Yang
Jwing Ming
Yangs Martial Arts Academy 1986

The Essence of T'ai Chi Ch'uan by Lo/Inn Amaker/Foe
North Atlantic Books 1985

Hara Diagnosis: Reflections on the Sea by Kiiko Matsumoto and
Steven Birch Paradigm Publications 1988

Five Elements and Ten Stems by Kiiko Matsumoto and Steven
Birch
Paradigm Publications

Combined Tai-Chi Chuan by Bow-Sim Mark
Chinese Wusu Research Institute 1979

The Tao of Tai Chi Chuan-Way To Rejuvenation by Jou Tsung
Hwa
Tai Chi Foundation 1980

Tao Te Ching by Gia by Fu Feng and Jane English
Vintage Books 1972

The Eight Extra Meridians Compiled by Kevin R. Jeynes B. Ac
Brisbane College of Traditional Acupuncture and Oriental
Medicine

The Secondary Vessels of Acupuncture by Royston Low
Thorsons Publishers Limited 1983

Extraordinary Vessels by Kiiko Matsumoto and Steven Birch
Paradigm Publications 1986

Tom Browns' Field Guide to Nature Observation and Tracking
by Tom Brown, Jr., with Brandt Morgan
Berkeley Books 1983

The I Ching or Book of Changes, by Wilhelm/Baynes
Princeton University Press 1967

Tai Chi Chuan and I Ching by Daliu
Harper and Row Publishers, Inc 1972

<u>Magnetic Healing and Meditation</u> by Larry Johnson O.M.D. C.A.
White Elephant Monastery 1988

<u>Eighteen Buddha Hands</u> by Wong Hon Fon
Lou Hun Gung—Praying Mantis Martial Arts Book Series #18
by Wong, Hon Fun
May Ngai Printing Company Hong Kong

Footnotes

[1] _Hara Diagnosis: Reflections on the Sea_ by Kiiko Matsumoto
and Steven Birch, page 44
Paradigm Publications 1988

[2] _Hara Diagnosis: Reflections on the Sea_ by Kiiko Matsumoto
and Steven Birch, page 156
Paradigm Publications 1988

[3] _Tao Te Ching_ 1st verse

[4] _Hara Diagnosis: Reflections on the Sea_ by Kiiko Matsumoto
and Steven Birch, page 71
Paradigm Publications 1988
    [4] (in above quote) Huai Nan 21, page 167

[5] _Hara Diagnosis: Reflections on the Sea_ by Kiiko Matsumoto
and Steven Birch, page 71
Paradigm Publications 1988
    [5] (in above quote) - Zou Yi, quoted from Ki No Shiso,
        page 238

[6] _The Theoretical Foundations of Chinese Medicine, Systems of
Correspondence_ by Manfred Porkert, pages 167-168
The Massachusetts Institute of Technology

[7] _Hara Diagnosis: Reflections on the Sea_ by Kiiko Matsumoto
and Steven Birch, page 71
Paradigm Publications 1988

[8] _The Theoretical Foundations of Chinese Medicine, Systems of
Correspondence_ by Manfred Porkert, page 173
The Massachusetts Institute of Technology

[9] _Hara Diagnosis: Reflections on the Sea_ by Kiiko Matsumoto
and Steven Birch, page 111
Paradigm Publications 1988

[10] _Hara Diagnosis: Reflections on the Sea_ by Kiiko Matsumoto
and Steven Birch, page 112
Paradigm Publications 1988

[11] <u>Hara Diagnosis: Reflections on the Sea</u> by Kiiko Matsumoto and Steven Birch, page 113
Paradigm Publications 1988

[12] <u>Hara Diagnosis: Reflections on the Sea</u> by Kiiko Matsumoto and Steven Birch, page 59
Paradigm Publications 1988

[13] <u>Five Elements and Ten Stems</u> by Kiiko Matsumoto and Steven Birch, page 67
Paradigm Publications

[14] <u>Hara Diagnosis: Reflections on the Sea</u> by Kiiko Matsumoto and Steven Birch, page 144
Paradigm Publications 1988
[29] (in the above quote) K. Mitsutane, Kaitai Hotsumou 3; 23-34

[15] <u>Hara Diagnosis: Reflections on the Sea</u> by Kiiko Matsumoto and Steven Birch, page 62
Paradigm Publications 1988

[16] <u>Hara Diagnosis: Reflections on the Sea</u> by Kiiko Matsumoto and Steven Birch, page 163
Paradigm Publications 1988

[17] <u>Hara Diagnosis: Reflections on the Sea</u> by Kiiko Matsumoto and Steven Birch, page 164
Paradigm Publications 1988
[7] (in the above quote) James Oschman, Natural Science of Healing, op.cit.

[18] <u>Hara Diagnosis: Reflections on the Sea</u> by Kiiko Matsumoto and Steven Birch, page 123
Paradigm Publications 1988

[19] <u>Hara Diagnosis: Reflections on the Sea</u> by Kiiko Matsumoto and Steven Birch, page 61
Paradigm Publications 1988
[8] (in the above quote) "ibid"= Sosen Hirooka Nangyo Tekkan, p 27-28 passim

[20] <u>Hara Diagnosis: Reflections on the Sea</u> by Kiiko Matsumoto and Steven Birch, page 83
Paradigm Publications 1988

[35] (in the above quote) Shuo Wen Jie Zi, quoted from Ki Wo Shiso, pg 27

[21] The Theoretical Foundations of Chinese Medicine, Systems of Correspondence by Manfred Porkert, page 189
The Massachusetts Institute of Technology

[22] The Theoretical Foundations of Chinese Medicine, Systems of Correspondence by Manfred Porkert, page 190
The Massachusetts Institute of Technology

[23] Magnetic Healing and Meditation by Larry Johnson O.M.D. C.A., page 166-119
White Elephant Monastery 1988

[24] Magnetic Healing and Meditation by Larry Johnson O.M.D. C.A., page 4
White Elephant Monastery 1988

[25] Magnetic Healing and Meditation by Larry Johnson O.M.D. C.A., page 113
White Elephant Monastery 1988

[26] Magnetic Healing and Meditation by Larry Johnson O.M.D. C.A., pages 8-10
White Elephant Monastery 1988

[27] 2Fundamentals of Tai Chi Chuan by Nen-Shau Huang, page 63
South Sky Book Company, 1974

[28] The Tao of Tai Chi Chuan-Way To Rejuvenation by Jou Tsung Hwa, page 106
Tai Chi Foundation 1980

[29] The correlation of the hexagrams to the postures came from Tai Chi Chuan and I Ching by Da Liu
Harper and Row Publishers, Inc.

[30] Wu Style Tai Ji Quan by Wang Peisheng & Zeng Weiqi, page 217
Hai Feng Publishing Co & Zhaohua Publishing House 1983

[31] <u>Wu Style Tai Ji Quan</u> by Wang Peisheng & Zeng Weiqi, page 94
Hai Feng Publishing Co & Zhaohua Publishing House 1983

[32] <u>T'ai Chi Ch'uan Ta Wen</u> by Chen Wei-Ming
Translated by Benjamin Pang Jeng Lo and Robert Smith, page 21
North Atlantic Books 1985

[33] <u>T'ai Chi Ch'uan Ta Wen</u> by Chen Wei-Ming
Translated by Benjamin Pang Jeng Lo and Robert Smith, page 55
North Atlantic Books 1985

[34] <u>Advanced Yang Style Tai Chi Chuan Volume One</u> by Yang Jwing Ming, pages 59-60
Yangs Martial Arts Academy 1986

[35] <u>Cheng Man-Ch'ings Advanced Tai—Chi Form Instructions</u>
Compiled and Translated by Douglas Wile, page 15
Sweet Ch'i Press 1985

[36] <u>Tom Browns' Field Guide to Nature Observation and Tracking</u> by Tom Brown, Jr., with Brandt Morgan, page 25
Berkeley Books 1983

[37] <u>Tom Browns' Field Guide to Nature Observation and Tracking</u> by Tom Brown, Jr., with Brandt Morgan, page 25
Berkeley Books 1983

[38] <u>The Essence of T'ai Chi Ch'uan</u> by Lo/Inn Amaker/Foe, pages 9-10
North Atlantic Books 1985

[39] <u>The Essence of T'ai Chi Ch'uan</u> by Lo/Inn Amaker/Foe, page 19
North Atlantic Books 1985

[40] <u>Advanced Yang Style Tai Chi Chuan Volume One</u> by Yang Jwing Ming
Yangs Martial Arts Academy 1986

Order Form

White Elephant Monastery
P.O. Box 523
San Francisco, CA 94101

Energetic Tai Chi Chuan at $9.95 each _____

Magnetic Healing and Meditation at $12.95 each _____

California residents add 6.5% sales tax _____

Shipping and handling:

Book Rate   First book $1.50 _____

                   Each additional book $1.00 _____

Air Mail $3.00 each book _____

                                    Total _____

Enclosed find my check or money order for _____ to cover
the cost of _____ copies of Energetic Tai Chi Chuan and/or
_____ copies of Magnetic Healing and Meditation plus tax (if
CA resident) and shipping.

Please send books to:

Name _____

Address _____

City/State _____Zip _____

Outside U.S. - Air Mail Only

Foreign orders must be prepaid at current exchange rates in
U.S. dollars.

Contact White Elephant Monastery for seminars and group
consultations!